THE *ULTIMATE*
HCG Diet
COOKBOOK

Make Every Bite Count with 500 Scrumptious Recipes Bursting with Flavor

There are other cookbooks that offer recipes suitable for the HCG diet plan. What makes this cookbook unique is that it gives you the opportunity to add FLAVOR and CREATIVITY to your food!

Enjoy food and full flavors and lose weight permanently by pairing this cookbook with the proven success of the HCG Protocol.

Janet Wilson & Terrie McDonald

Total Health Is Natural, Inc./ThinNow

Janet Wilson & Terrie McDonald, Co-Owners
Total Health Is Natural, Inc./ThinNow

Visit us at www.ThinNow.com

Published in the United States of America

First Printing: January 2012

ISBN 978-0-9830183-0-8

ATTENTION RETAILERS:
This book is available at a quantity discount with bulk purchase of 20 books or more. For information, please contact Total Health Is Natural, Inc. at 1-888-424-5220 or cookbook@ThinNow.com.

Salut! Bon Appétit!

When food is plain and has no flavor,
You crave a dish that you can savor!
The answers are within this book
You'll be astounded, take a look!

There's Citrus Thyme Encrusted Fish
Soups, Kebabs—it's all delish!
Soy-Glazed Shrimp with Apricot
Diet food? Your tongue says not!

Curried Salad with a crunch
Enjoy it for dinner or for lunch!
Orange Beef, Greek Chicken Stew—
We love the flavors, you will, too!

The gift of health to you from us,
We think you are fabulous!
We're pleased to share these recipes
And say, Salut! Bon Appétit!

This cookbook was created by two people who have been in your shoes!
After experiencing how little variety and flavor the HCG diet plan offered,
we loaded up on bottles of Capella and Stevia flavor drops, consulted a pro-
fessional chef, and started creating.

After lots of mixing, cooking, and tasting, we ended up with more than
800 ways to pump up the flavor while following the HCG diet plan. This
book is jam-packed with more than 500 recipes and modifications, and we
offer hundreds more to our clients and Facebook friends.

You do not have to navigate the challenging waters of the HCG diet plan
on your own! Make the process of planning, cooking, and eating far more
enjoyable by bringing this invaluable resource into your kitchen. Now you
can look forward to recipes that make your mouth water and your stomach
feel satisfied!

Introduction

FOR MANY PEOPLE, the restrictive list of foods on the HCG Protocol can be challenging to follow. It's not easy to create enough variety and flavor to be satisfying for the duration of the diet. Let's face it—on a low-calorie diet you have to make every bite count!

Luckily, you have thousands of delicious flavor options with Stevia and Capella flavor drops. These drops contain no fat, calories, carbs, or sweeteners, yet add a world of flavor to any food. With flavors such as Cinnamon Danish Swirl, Banana Split, Chocolate Fudge Brownie, and Vanilla Crème, your HCG diet food choices are lifted to an entirely new level.

Add savory flavors such as Butter and Sizzlin' Bacon, and there is no end to what you can create in the kitchen. You'll hardly know you're on a diet!

Both the Capella and Stevia drops add pizzazz to a morning protein shake or a touch of zing to an otherwise bland protein serving. Whether you need a touch of sweet or the taste of nuts, berries, baked goods, and more, these drops will wake up your diet-dulled taste buds!

Enjoy the Vanilla Crème Stevia in Caramel Baked Pears or Poached Lobster with Strawberry Vanilla Cream Sauce. Create a tantalizing Classic Chili Mole with Chocolate Fudge Brownie drops. Have a Peanut Butter Banana Frittata for breakfast, and mix up shakes with flavors like Hazelnut or Peaches & Cream.

Capella and Stevia flavor drops allow you to luxuriate in mouth-watering flavor while you lose weight!

Inside this cookbook you will find more than 500 recipes and modifications that incorporate Capella and Stevia flavor drops to ramp up the flavor from bland to enticing. You will find not only flavorful recipes, but tips, resources, and coaching to help you succeed on your journey to lose weight.

The HCG Protocol does not have to be a struggle, or simply a means to an end. By using this cookbook as a partner in your journey, from VLCD through the end of Maintenance and beyond, you can look forward to trying new recipe creations and actually enjoying your meals.

We invite you to move beyond the limited food lists of the HCG Protocol by making beverages, dishes, and entire meals that will keep you motivated to continue and successfully complete your weight-loss journey.

Table of Contents

HCG PROTOCOL
VLCD (Very Low Calorie Diet) Phase

WE BEGIN THIS SECTION WITH the list of foods allowed during the VLCD portion of the HCG Protocol, along with the calorie count and the appropriate serving of each type of vegetable. Up to 500 calories per day are allowed.

If you are following a modified HCG diet plan of 800 or more daily calories, simply increase your serving size or eat an additional meal to meet your caloric requirement. We recommend including a partial or full serving of protein with every meal.

Breakfast: Tea or coffee in any quantity. One tablespoon of milk (11 calories) allowed per day. Stevia (0 calories) is the only sweetener that is not shown to slow weight loss; we recommend Sweetleaf and KAL brands because there are no additives. Truvia, Purevia, and Stevia in the Raw are *not* pure and can slow weight loss.

Lunch & Dinner: Choose ONE item from each section, preferably different choices for lunch and dinner.

(1) **Protein: 100 grams (3.5 oz.) of one lean meat or white fish.** All meat should be weighed raw, no bone, and trimmed of all visible fat. Meat can be grilled, baked, broiled, or pan "fried" without oil or fat.

Beef, Chicken, Other Protein
Steak (trimmed to 0% fat) – 192 calories
Ground Beef (95% lean) – 137 calories
Roast Beef (lean, trimmed) – 140 calories
Beef Kidney – 99 calories
Buffalo – 100 calories
Veal – 120 calories
Chicken Breast – 110 calories

Egg* (1 whole + 3 whites) – 138 calories
Cottage Cheese* (½ cup, no fat) – 75 calories
Whey Protein Shake* (0–5 carbs) – 80–100 calories

*This group of foods is allowed up to 3 times per week.

Fish
Cod – 95 Calories
Wild Chilean Sea Bass – 97 calories
Wild Flounder – 91 calories
Wild Sole – 91 calories
Wild Halibut – 110 calories

Seafood
Lobster – 90 calories
Crab – 84 caloriesShrimp or Prawns – 105 calories
Crawfish – 74 calories

(2) **Vegetables:** Choose **ONLY ONE** vegetable per meal. **NO MIXING.**

Lettuces of any kind
 (2 cups raw) – 15 calories
Spinach
 (3 cups raw) – 21 calories
Asparagus
 (2 cups raw) – 54 calories
Cabbage
 (2 cups raw) – 44 calories
Tomatoes
 (1 cup cherry) – 18 calories
Tomato
 (1 medium) – 22 calories
Cucumbers
 (2 cups/peel optional) – 32 calories

Chard
 (2 cups raw) – 14 calories
Onions
 (1 cup raw) – 64 calories
Beet Greens
 (2 cups raw) – 16 calories
Red Radishes
 (2 cups raw) – 40 calories
Celery
 (2 cups raw) – 32 calories
Fennel
 (1.5 cups raw) – 40 calories
Chicory Greens
 (2 cups raw) – 15 calories

(3) **Fruit**: Two servings allowed per day, not at the same meal, 4 to 6 hours apart.

Apple
  (1 medium/3" diameter) –
  95 calories
Orange
  (1 medium/3" diameter) –
  70 calories

Grapefruit
  (½ medium) – 52 calories
Strawberries
  (10½-inch) – 40 calories

(4) **Breadstick (Grissini) or Melba toast**: Two servings per day, not at the same meal, 4 to 6 hours apart.
Grissini breadstick (1 regular or 2 thin) OR Melba toast (1 rectangular or 2 rounds) – 20 to 25 calories

Beverages: Plain spring water, mineral water, tea, and coffee in any quantity at any time. Chicken, beef, fish, or vegetable broth (about 20 calories per cup) must be made with VLCD veggies. **Drink 75 to 100 ounces of water per day.**

The **juice of one lemon** (12 calories) is allowed per day. **Seasonings** are allowed except pre-mixed spices as they often contain sugar. You may use **Bragg Liquid Aminos, mustard** (water, mustard seed, vinegar, turmeric), **Frank's Original Hot Sauce**, and **Spry Xylitol gum or mints** (1.2 calories each).

No substitutions. Any food may be eliminated due to lack of hunger, starting with Melba toast/Grissini and/or one or more servings of fruit. **It is important to eat the two 3.5-ounce servings of protein and the two servings of vegetables daily.**

* Allowed occasionally – up to three times per week

VLCD Sample Meal Plan for 26-Day HCG Protocol

Load Days 1 & 2: HCG: 0.5 ml. 6x/day. Consume High Fats: – Cream – Butter – Nuts – Avocado – Olive Oil – Ice Cream	**VLCD Days:** Breakfast: 1 Fruit (optional), Tea, Coffee, Water. Drink 75 to 100 oz. water each day.	**VLCD Day 1** HCG: 0.5 ml. 6x/day. Lunch: **Classic Spinach Salad** Dinner: **Quick Chinese Orange Beef & Cabbage**	**Day 2** HCG: 0.5 ml. 6x/day. Lunch: **Fabulous French Onion Soup (add leftover beef)** Dinner: **New Orleans BBQ Shrimp**	**Day 3** HCG: 0.5 ml. 6x/day. Lunch: **New Orleans BBQ Shrimp** Dinner: **Chicken and Asparagus with Peanut Sauce**	**Day 4** HCG: 0.5 ml. 6x/day. Lunch: **Chicken and Asparagus with Peanut Sauce** Dinner: **Tandoori Shrimp salad**	**Day 5** HCG: 0.5 ml. 6x/day. Lunch: **Applewood Bacon Chicken Filet** Dinner: **Skewered Steak and Onions**
Day 6 HCG: 0.5 ml. 6x/day. Lunch: **Crunchy Curried Chicken Salad** Dinner: **Teriyaki Sea Bass with Napa Cabbage**	**Day 7** HCG: 0.5 ml. 6x/day. Lunch: **Hot Sweet/Sour Chinese Beef Soup** Dinner: **Chicken Fajita Wraps**	**Day 8** HCG: 0.5 ml. 6x/day. Lunch: **Chicken Fajita Wraps** Dinner: **Spicy Coconut Ceviche**	**Day 9** HCG: 0.5 ml. 6x/day. Lunch: **Strawberry Butter Leaf Salad with Hazelnut Dressing – with Grilled Chicken** Dinner: **Nonna's Garlic Meatballs in Tomato Sauce**	**Day 10** HCG: 0.5 ml. 6x/day. Lunch: **: Nonna's Garlic Meatballs in Tomato Sauce** Dinner: **Chicken and Spinach Meatloaf**	**Day 11** HCG: 0.5 ml. 6x/day. Lunch: **Chicken and Spinach Meatloaf** Dinner: **Citrus Thyme Crusted Fish**	**Day 12** HCG: 0.5 ml. 6x/day. Lunch: **Broiled Lobster, Grapefruit & Endive Salad** Dinner: **Tropical Oven "Fried" Chicken Cucumber & Orange Salad**
Day 13 HCG: 0.5 ml. 6x/day. Lunch: **Tropical Oven "Fried" Chicken, Orange Glazed Asparagus** Dinner: **Sweet & Sour Stuffed Cabbage**	**Day 14** HCG: 0.5 ml. 6x/day. Lunch: **Crunchy Curried Chicken Salad** Dinner: **Maple Glazed Veal with Apples**	**Day 15** HCG: 0.5 ml. 6x/day. Lunch: **Amaretto Baked Fish with Orange Zest** Dinner: **Stir Fried Lemon Chicken with Chard**	**Day 16** HCG: 0.5 ml. 6x/day. Lunch: **Stir Fried Lemon Chicken with Chard** Dinner: **Apricot Soy Glazed Shrimp**	**Day 17** HCG: 0.5 ml. 6x/day. Lunch: **Shrimp with Sweet and Smoky Tomato Sauce** Dinner: **Classic Chili Mole**	**Day 18** HCG: 0.5 ml. 6x/day. Lunch: **Classic Chili Mole** Dinner: **Apple Stuffed Chicken Breast**	**Day 19** HCG: 0.5 ml. 6x/day. Lunch: **Apple Stuffed Chicken Breast** Dinner: **Petit Baked Crab Cakes**
Day 20 HCG: 0.5 ml. 6x/day. Lunch: **Broiled Lobster/Grapefruit and Endive Salad** Dinner: **Big Bodacious Burger with Tangy Apple Slaw**	**Day 21** HCG: 0.5 ml. 6x/day. Lunch: **Spanish Style Crab Stew** Dinner: **Greek Cinnamon Chicken**	**Day 22** HCG: 0.5 ml. 6x/day. Lunch: **Greek Cinnamon Chicken** Dinner: **Persian-Style Meatballs with Cabbage**	**Day 23** HCG: 0.5 ml. 6x/day. Lunch: **Persian-Style Meatballs with Cabbage** Dinner: **Quick Lobster Stir-Fry with Spring Onions**	**Day 24** NO HCG DROPS Lunch: **Three Alarm Buffalo Tenders with Celery Sticks** Dinner: **Oven-Roasted Fish with Fennel**	**Day 25** NO HCG DROPS Lunch: **Orange Beef & Asparagus Negimaki** Dinner: **Curried Chicken and Onions**	**Day 26** NO HCG DROPS Start M1 tomorrow! Lunch: **Curried Chicken and Onions** Dinner: **Tuscan Bistecca with Lemon Romaine Salad/ Grissini**

VLCD RECIPES
for the HCG Protocol

ALL OF THE **VLCD** RECIPES in this book follow the HCG Protocol as written by Dr. A. T. W. Simeons in *Pounds and Inches: A New Approach to Obesity*. Dr. Simeons' manuscript is the original and only HCG Protocol that has years of research and case studies to back it up.

This journey, when followed precisely, will deliver you quickly and safely to your goal of a healthy body, free of excess fat. Along the way, you deserve to eat food that tastes good! Never boring and always flavorful, these recipes will keep you motivated and satisfied.

COLD DRINKS

OOL AND REFRESHING BEVERAGES are everyone's lifesaver on any type of diet, but are particularly welcome on the HCG Protocol. With restrictions as they are, a deliciously satisfying and thirst-quenching drink can be nearly as pleasing as a snack or dessert and can make a real difference in your success at sticking with the plan.

Thanks to the wonderful variety of Capella and Stevia, tempting sweet and tasty beverages await. Mixed with fizzy water for terrific sodas, or stirred into teas or infused concoctions, the cold drinks in this chapter are guaranteed to keep your taste buds entertained and your thirst at bay. So, drink up and enjoy!

Orange Ade
(Recipe on page 5)

Sensational Sodas

Super Vanilla Cream Soda
Add 5 drops Capella French Vanilla and 8 drops Clear Stevia to 8 oz. (1 cup) sparkling water, such as Perrier. Stir well, add ice, or blend with ice as a slushy, and enjoy.

Clear Crisp Cola
Add 4 drops Capella Cola and 6 to 8 drops Clear Stevia to 8 oz. (1 cup) sparkling water, such as Perrier. Stir, add ice, or blend with ice as a slushy, and enjoy.

All Natural Root Beer
Add 5 drops Capella Root Beer Float and 8 drops Clear Stevia to 8 oz. (1 cup) sparkling water, such as Perrier. Stir, add ice, or blend with ice as a slushy, and enjoy.

Cool Coconut Fizz
Add 5 drops Capella Coconut and 8 drops Clear Stevia (or more to taste) to 8 oz. (1 cup) sparkling water, such as Perrier. Stir, add ice, or blend with ice as a slushy, and enjoy.

Tropical Fizz
Combine the juice of ½ a grapefruit with 8 oz. (1 cup) sparkling water, such as Perrier. Add 4 drops each Capella Coconut and Capella Banana Split, 2 to 3 drops Capella Orange Creamsicle, and 8 drops Clear Stevia. Stir well, add ice, or blend with ice as a slushy, and enjoy.

Italian Citrus Soda
Add 5 drops Capella Orange Creamsicle, 4 drops Capella Lemon-Lime, and 8 drops Clear Stevia to 8 oz. (1 cup) sparkling water, such as Perrier. Stir well, add ice, or blend with ice as a slushy, and enjoy.

Real Ginger Ale
Steep a ¼-inch piece of fresh gingerroot in ¼ cup boiling water for 10 minutes. Strain into a glass filled with ice and add 8 oz. (1 cup) sparkling water such as Perrier. Stir in 5 drops Capella French Vanilla and sweeten to taste with Clear Stevia.

Peachy Cream Soda

Add 3 drops Capella Peaches & Cream, 3 drops Capella Vanilla Custard, and 8 drops Clear Stevia to 8 oz. (1 cup) sparkling water, such as Perrier. Stir well, add ice, or blend with ice as a slushy, and enjoy.

Mock Mountain Dew

Add 3 to 5 drops Capella Lemon Lime and 2 drops Capella French Vanilla to 8 oz. (1 cup) sparkling water. Sweeten to taste with Clear Stevia, stir, and enjoy.

Green Apple Lemonade

Add 3 to 5 drops Capella Green Apple to 8 oz. (1 cup) cold water. Stir in juice of ½ a lemon, sweeten to taste with Clear Stevia, and enjoy.

Sweet Berry Cherry Cola

Add 4 drops Capella Sweet Strawberry and 4 drops Capella Cherry Cola to 8 oz. (1 cup) plain sparkling water. Sweeten to taste with Clear Stevia, stir, and enjoy.

French Vanilla Cherry Coke

Add 3 drops Capella French Vanilla and 3 to 5 drops Capella Cherry Coke to 8 oz. (1 cup) plain sparkling water. Sweeten to taste with Clear Stevia, stir, and enjoy.

Infusions and Ades

Strawberry Ice Cubes

Fill a standard ice tray with purified water. Add 1 drop Capella Strawberries & Cream (or Raspberry, if preferred) and 2 drops Clear Stevia to each cube and insert half a small strawberry in each. Freeze and use in plain water, iced teas, or Fruit Punch (below).

Fruit Punch

Fill a glass with Strawberry Ice Cubes. Add 8 oz. (1 cup) purified water, 5 drops Strawberries & Cream (or Raspberry, if preferred), 8 drops Clear Stevia, and the juice of half an orange. Stir well and enjoy.

Lemony Lemonade

Add juice of half a lemon and 10 to 12 drops Sweetleaf Stevia Lemon Drop to 8 oz. (1 cup) purified water. Stir, add ice, and enjoy.

Orange Ade

Combine the juice of 1 orange and 1 cup purified water in a glass. Add 6 to 8 drops Sweetleaf Stevia Valencia Orange and stir well. Add ice, and enjoy.

Apple Tonic Fusion

Place 3 slices of apple and 1 white tea bag in an 8-oz. measuring cup. Fill with boiling water and steep for 3 minutes. Strain into a glass filled with ice and add 3 drops Capella French Vanilla and 6 drops Clear Stevia. Stir, garnish with an apple slice, and enjoy.

Cool Cucumber Tonic

Place half a sliced cucumber in 2 cups of purified water and allow to chill for 3 hours or overnight. Remove the cucumbers, pour liquid into an ice-filled glass, add 4 to 6 drops Sweetleaf Stevia Lemon Drop and 2 sprigs fresh mint; stir well. Garnish with a cucumber slice and enjoy.

Puckered Smooching on the Beach

Combine the juice of ½ a grapefruit with ⅔ cup purified water. Pour into an ice-filled glass, add 3 to 5 drops Capella Raspberry and 6 drops Clear Stevia. Stir well and enjoy.

Iced Teas and Coffees

Orange Delight Iced Tea

Add 10 to 12 drops Sweetleaf Stevia Valencia Orange to 8 oz. (1 cup) plain unsweetened iced tea. Stir, add ice, garnish with an orange slice, and enjoy.

Fizzy Iced Green Tea with Lemon

Add 8 to 10 drops Sweetleaf Stevia Lemon Drop to 8 oz. (1 cup) strong brewed cold green tea. Top with a splash of sparkling water. Stir, add ice, garnish with a lemon slice, and enjoy.

Cranberry Iced Tea

Add 6 to 8 drops Capella Cranberry to 10 to 12 oz. chilled plain tea. Sweeten to taste with Clear Stevia and serve.

Herbal Iced Cooler

Add 3 drops Capella Orange Creamsicle, 4 drops Capella Raspberry, and 8 drops Clear Stevia to 8 oz. (1 cup) of your choice of strongly brewed cold herbal tea. Add a splash of sparkling water. Stir, add ice, garnish with a mint sprig, and enjoy.

Icy White Tea with Strawberries

Add 3 to 5 drops Capella Strawberries & Cream and 6 drops Clear Stevia to 8 oz. (1 cup) cold white tea. Add 3 or 4 Strawberry Ice Cubes, stir, and enjoy.

Apricot Iced Tea

Add 12 to 15 drops Sweetleaf Stevia Apricot Nectar to 8 oz. (1 cup) plain unsweetened tea. Stir well, add ice, garnish with a lemon slice, and enjoy.

Peachy Keen Tea

Add 5 drops Capella Peaches & Cream and 8 drops Clear Stevia to 8 oz. (1 cup) plain unsweetened tea. Stir well, add ice, and enjoy.

Blueberry Iced Green Tea

Add 3 drops Capella Blueberry to 8 oz. (1 cup) plain green tea. Sweeten to taste with Clear Stevia, pour over ice, and enjoy.

Chocolate Iced Coffee

Add 5 drops Capella Chocolate Fudge Brownie, 2 drops Capella French Vanilla, and 7 drops Clear Stevia to 8 oz. (1 cup) cold coffee. Stir in 1 Tbsp. milk, add ice, and enjoy.

Caramel Crème Iced Coffee

Add 4 or 5 drops Capella Caramel, 3 drops Capella Vanilla Custard, and 8 drops Clear Stevia to 8 oz. (1 cup) cold coffee. Stir, add ice, and enjoy.

HOT DRINKS

DELIGHTFULLY FRAGRANT AND FLAVORFUL, hot beverages can be just the ticket for starting the day as an afternoon pick-me-up or ending the night on a soothing note. Coffees, teas, and hot infusions get a real burst of flavor from the wide variety of Capella and Stevia drops. From chocolate creations to fruity and exotic quaffs, you'll find a hot beverage in this chapter that's guaranteed to hit the spot on its own or with a meal.

When creating coffees and teas, be sure to use as many organic versions as possible, preferably using purified water to brew and steep. Drinks that call for milk count as your daily milk allowance. For additional sweetness in any selection, add a few extra drops of Clear Stevia to taste.

Pumpkin Spice Latte
(Recipe on page 10)

Coffee House Favorites

Milk Chocolate Toffee Hazelnut Latte

Add 3 drops each Capella Milk Chocolate Toffee and Capella Hazelnut to 8 oz. (1 cup) hot coffee. Stir in 1 Tbsp. milk, sweeten to taste with Clear Stevia, and enjoy.

Coconut Fudge Latte

Add 4 or 5 drops Capella Coconut and 2 or 3 drops Capella Chocolate Fudge Brownie to 8 oz. (1 cup) hot coffee. Stir in 1 Tbsp. milk and sweeten to taste with Clear Stevia, and enjoy.

Caramel Cream Latte

Add 4 or 5 drops Capella Caramel and 10 drops Sweetleaf Stevia Vanilla Crème to 8 oz. (1 cup) hot coffee. Stir in 1 Tbsp. milk and sweeten to taste with Clear Stevia, and enjoy.

Chocolate Éclair Latte

Add 4 drops each Capella Chocolate Fudge Brownie and Capella Vanilla Custard to 8 oz. (1 cup) hot coffee. Stir in 1 Tbsp. milk and sweeten to taste with 6 to 8 drops Clear Stevia, and enjoy.

English Toffee Coffee

Add 4 drops Capella Caramel, 2 drops Capella Milk Chocolate Toffee, and 8 drops Clear Stevia to 8 oz. (1 cup) hot coffee. Stir in 1 Tbsp. milk and enjoy.

Chocolate Raspberry Café

Add 4 drops each Capella Chocolate Fudge Brownie and Capella Raspberry and 8 drops Clear Stevia to 8 oz. (1 cup) hot coffee. Stir and enjoy.

Sweet Dark Mocha

Add 5 drops Capella Chocolate Fudge Brownie and 8 drops Clear Stevia to 8 oz. (1 cup) hot coffee. Stir and enjoy.

Minty Irish Cream Coffee

Add 3 drops Capella Spearmint and 3 drops Capella Irish Cream to 8 oz. (1 cup) hot coffee. Stir in 1 Tbsp. milk, sweeten to taste with Clear Stevia, and enjoy.

Vanilla Irish Cream Coffee

Add 3 drops Capella Irish Cream and 8 drops Sweetleaf Stevia Vanilla Crème to 8 oz. (1 cup) hot coffee. Stir in 1 Tbsp. milk and sweeten to taste with Clear Stevia, and enjoy.

Amaretto Cream Latte

Add 3 to 5 drops Capella Amaretto and 8 drops Sweetleaf Stevia Vanilla Crème to 8 oz. (1 cup) hot coffee. Stir in 1 Tbsp. milk and enjoy.

Gingerbread Latte

Add 3 to 5 drops Capella Gingerbread to 8 oz. (1 cup) hot coffee. Stir in 1 Tbsp. milk, sweeten to taste with Clear Stevia, and enjoy.

Cinnamon Bun Café

Add 4 drops Capella Cinnamon Danish Swirl and 6 drops Sweetleaf Stevia Cinnamon to 8 oz. (1 cup) hot coffee. Stir in 1 Tbsp. milk, sweeten to taste with Clear Stevia, and enjoy.

Pumpkin Spice Latte

Add 3 to 5 drops Capella Pumpkin Pie Spice to 8 oz. (1 cup) hot coffee. Stir in 1 Tbsp. milk, sweeten to taste with Clear Stevia, and enjoy.

Italian Eggnog Latte

Add 3 to 5 drops Capella Italian Egg Nog to 8 oz. (1 cup) hot coffee. Stir in 1 Tbsp. milk, sweeten to taste with Clear Stevia, and enjoy.

Teas and Toddies

Lemon Lift Green Tea

Add 10 to 12 drops Sweetleaf Stevia Lemon Drop to 8 oz. (1 cup) hot green tea. Stir and enjoy.

Chocolate Mint Delight

Add 5 drops Capella Dutch Chocolate Mint and 8 drops Clear Stevia to 8 oz. (1 cup) hot brewed herbal mint tea. Stir and enjoy.

Sweet Lemon Ginger Tea

Brew together 1 plain teabag and a ¼-inch piece of fresh gingerroot. Strain and add 10 drops Sweetleaf Stevia Lemon Drop. Stir and enjoy.

Triple Lemon Soother

Add 10 to 12 drops Sweetleaf Stevia Lemon Drop to 8 oz. (1 cup) herbal lemon tea. Add a slice of fresh lemon, stir, and enjoy.

Warm Blueberry Cobbler

Add 3 drops Capella Blueberry and 3 drops Capella Vanilla Custard to 8 oz. (1 cup) hot blueberry herbal tea. Stir, sweeten to taste with Clear Stevia, and enjoy.

Warm Apple Pie à la Mode

Add 3 to 5 drops Capella Apple Pie and 8 drops Sweetleaf Stevia Vanilla Crème to 8 oz. (1 cup) hot brewed apple-flavored herbal tea. Stir in 1 Tbsp. milk and sweeten to taste with Clear Stevia, and enjoy.

Hot Spiced Apple Cider

Add 3 drops Capella Hot Cinnamon Candy to 8 oz. (1 cup) hot brewed apple-flavored herbal tea. Sweeten to taste with Clear Stevia, stir well, and garnish with an apple slice, and enjoy.

Apricot and Peach Cobbler Toddy

Add 8 drops Sweetleaf Stevia Apricot Nectar and 3 drops Capella Peaches & Cream to 8 oz. (1 cup) hot brewed plain white tea, and enjoy.

Pralines and Cream Hot Toddy

Add 3 to 5 drops Capella Pralines & Cream and 3 drops Capella Irish Cream to 8 oz. (1 cup) hot chamomile tea. Sweeten to taste with Clear Stevia, and enjoy.

Green Apple Spiced Cider

Add 3 to 5 drops Capella Green Apple and 3 drops Capella Pumpkin Pie Spice to 8 oz. (1 cup) Constant Comment hot tea. Sweeten with Clear Stevia to taste and enjoy.

Chocolatey Chai

8 oz. (1 cup) purified water	1 cinnamon stick
1 plain teabag	4 whole black peppercorns
2 whole cloves	1 tablespoon milk
1 cardamom pod	10 to 12 drops Sweetleaf Stevia Chocolate

1. Bring water to boil in a small saucepan. Remove from heat and stir in teabag, cloves, cardamom, cinnamon, peppercorns, milk, and Stevia drops.
2. Allow to steep for 5 minutes, then strain and serve.

Orange Spiced Tea

8 oz. (1 cup) purified water	One 1-inch piece of orange peel
1 plain teabag	10 drops Sweetleaf Stevia Valencia Orange
2 whole cloves	
1 small cinnamon stick	

1. Bring water to boil in a small saucepan. Remove from heat and add teabags, cloves, cinnamon, and orange peel.
2. Allow to steep for 5 minutes.
3. Strain into mug or teacup. Add Stevia drops. Stir and enjoy.

Chamomile Hot Toddy

Add 10 to 12 drops Stevia English Toffee and 3 drops Capella Vanilla Custard to 8 oz. (1 cup) hot chamomile tea. Stir and enjoy.

Blueberry Cinnamon Crumble From the Oven

Add 4 drops Capella Blueberry Cinnamon Crumble and 5 drops Stevia Cinnamon to 8 oz. (1 cup) hot steeped Blueberry flavored tea. Stir in 1 tablespoon milk, sweeten to taste with Clear Stevia, and enjoy.

SMOOTHIES AND PROTEIN SHAKES

RICH AND FILLING SMOOTHIES AND SHAKES can be very satisfying remedies when hunger pangs hit. Blended or whisked into delicious treats, these selections will serve you well during the sometimes challenging VLCD phase.

Thanks to the terrific flavor selection of Capella and Stevia, there are many ways you can doctor up fruit drinks and protein shakes, whether using plain protein powder or a flavored version. Just remember to count the drinks with cottage cheese and those with protein powder toward your protein selection.

Creamy Strawberry Smoothie
(Recipe on page 15)

Smoothies

Creamsicle Smoothie

Juice of 1 orange | ½ cup purified water, well chilled
1 Tbsp. milk | 10 to 12 drops Sweetleaf Stevia Valencia Orange
3 to 4 ice cubes | 8 to 10 drops Sweetleaf Stevia Vanilla Crème

Combine all ingredients in a blender and puree on high until smooth. Pour into a glass and enjoy. (70 calories; 1 fruit, 1 milk)

Creamy Strawberry Smoothie

½ cup purified water, well chilled | 5 strawberries, stemmed and halved
½ cup nonfat cottage cheese |
4 Strawberry Ice Cubes (Recipe on page 4) | 12 to 15 drops Sweetleaf Stevia Berry

Combine all ingredients in a blender and puree on high until smooth. Pour into a glass and enjoy. (115 calories; 1 protein, 1 fruit)

Orange Banana Smoothie

½ cup purified water, well chilled | ½ orange, cut into segments (pulp and seeds removed)
½ cup nonfat cottage cheese |
3 ice cubes | 6 drops Sweetleaf Stevia Valencia Orange
3 drops Capella Banana |

Combine all ingredients in a blender and puree on high until smooth. Pour into a glass, sweeten to taste with Clear Stevia, and enjoy. (110 calories; 1 protein, ½ fruit)

Peachy Almond Smoothie

½ cup purified water, well chilled | 3 drops Capella Peaches & Cream
½ cup nonfat cottage cheese | 3 drops Capella Amaretto
3 ice cubes | 8 to 10 drops Clear Stevia

Combine all ingredients in a blender and puree on high until smooth. Pour into a glass, sweeten to taste with Clear Stevia, and enjoy. (75 calories; 1 protein)

Shakes

Strawberry Banana Power Shake

5 strawberries, stemmed and
   halved
1 level scoop (28 grams) 0–5 carb
   whey protein powder
¾ cup purified water, well chilled

3 to 4 ice cubes
10 to 12 drops Sweetleaf Stevia
   Berry
4 drops Capella Banana Split
Clear Stevia drops to taste

Combine all ingredients in a blender and puree on high until smooth. Pour into a glass and enjoy. (107 calories; 1 protein, 1 fruit)

Quick Chocolate Caramel Shake

¾ cup purified water, well chilled
1 level scoop (28 grams) 0–5 carb
   whey protein powder

10 to 12 drops Sweetleaf Stevia
   Chocolate
4 drops Capella Caramel
Clear Stevia drops to taste

In a small bowl, whisk together the water and protein powder. Stir in the chocolate and caramel drops. Sweeten to taste with Clear Stevia, pour into an 8-oz. glass, and enjoy. (87 calories; 1 protein)

Banana Cream Pie Shake

¾ cup purified water, well chilled
1 level scoop (28 grams) 0–5 carb
   whey protein powder
1 Tbsp. milk

5 drops Capella Banana Split
3 drops Capella Vanilla Custard
8 drops Clear Stevia, or more to
   taste

Combine all ingredients and whisk together in a small bowl or puree in a blender on high until smooth. Pour into a glass and enjoy. (87 calories; 1 protein, 1 milk)

Iced Chocolate Hazelnut Cappuccino

3 to 4 oz. purified water
1 level scoop (28 grams) 0–5 carb
   chocolate whey protein powder

3 drops Capella Hazelnut
3 drops Capella Cappuccino
5 to 6 drops Clear Stevia

Whisk together the water and whey in a small bowl or combine in a shaker until smooth. Add Clear Stevia to taste, pour over ice, and enjoy. (87 calories; 1 protein)

Vanilla Eggnog Shake

3 to 4 oz. purified water
1 packet (25.5 grams) 0–5 carb
   vanilla whey protein powder

3 or 4 drops Capella Italian
   Eggnog
3 or 4 drops Clear Stevia

Whisk together the water and whey in a small bowl or combine in a shaker until smooth. Add Clear Stevia to taste, pour over ice, and enjoy. (87 calories; 1 protein)

Dutch Cocoa Mint Shake

3 to 4 oz. purified water
1 packet (25.5 grams) 0–5 carb
   chocolate whey protein powder

3 drops Capella Dutch Chocolate
   Mint
3 or 4 drops Clear Stevia

Combine the water and whey in a small bowl or combine in a shaker until smooth. Sweeten to taste with Clear Stevia, pour over ice, and enjoy. (87 calories; 1 protein)

Chocolate Peanut Butter Shake

3 to 4 oz. purified water
1 packet (25.5 grams) 0–5 carb
   chocolate whey protein powder

3 drops Capella Peanut Butter
5 or 6 drops Sweetleaf Stevia
   Chocolate

Whisk together the water and whey in a small bowl or combine in a shaker until smooth. Pour over ice and enjoy. (87 calories; 1 protein)

Orange Peach Power Shake

¾ cup purified water, well chilled
1 level scoop (28 grams) 0–5 carb
   whey protein powder
4 drops Capella Peaches & Cream

8 drops Sweetleaf Stevia
   Valencia Orange
3 or 4 drops Clear Stevia, or
   more to taste

Whisk together the water and whey in a small bowl or combine in a shaker until smooth. Sweeten to taste with Clear Stevia, pour over ice, and enjoy. (87 calories; 1 protein)

Vanilla Fudge Sundae Shake

3 to 4 oz. purified water

1 level scoop (28 grams) 0–5 carb vanilla whey protein powder

3 drops Capella French Vanilla

2 drops Capella Chocolate Fudge Brownie

3 or 4 drops Clear Stevia

Whisk together the water and whey in a small bowl or combine in a shaker until smooth. Sweeten to taste with Clear Stevia, pour over ice, and enjoy. (87 calories; 1 protein)

Cinnamon French Toast Super Shake

¾ cup purified water, well chilled

1 level scoop (28 grams) 0–5 carb whey protein powder

4 drops Capella French Toast

8 drops Sweetleaf Stevia Cinnamon

3 or 4 drops Clear Stevia, or more to taste

Whisk together the water and whey in a small bowl or combine in a shaker until smooth. Sweeten to taste with Clear Stevia, pour over ice, and enjoy. (87 calories; 1 protein)

Caramel Apple Power Shake

¾ cup purified water, well chilled

1 level scoop (28 grams) 0–5 carb whey protein powder

4 drops Capella Apple Pie

4 drops Capella Caramel

8 drops Clear Stevia, or more to taste

Combine the water and whey in a small bowl or in a shaker until smooth. Sweeten to taste with Clear Stevia, pour over ice, garnish with an apple slice, and enjoy. (87 calories; 1 protein)

S'mores in a Shake

4 oz. (½ cup) purified water

1 scoop (28 grams) 0–5 carb vanilla whey protein powder

3 drops Capella Graham Cracker

5 or 6 drops Sweetleaf Stevia Chocolate

Whisk together all ingredients in a small bowl or combine in a shaker until smooth. Pour over ice and enjoy.

SPLENDID SOUPS

HOMEMADE SOUPS CAN BE a satisfying and comforting choice for lunch or dinner, especially during the very low calorie phase of the HCG diet. Brimming with nourishment and flavor, soups that contain protein can become your main course, while those that are vegetable based can accompany a protein entrée. Be sure, however, to pair a chicken-broth-based soup with a chicken entrée, to stick with the same protein.

The first step in creating delicious soups is starting with a flavorful broth. At the beginning of this chapter are basic recipes for chicken, beef, fish, and vegetable broths that use VLCD ingredients. With the enhancement of vegetables and aromatic herbs, you will be surprised at the amazingly appetizing results. Use these broths as a base for the soups that follow and as an ingredient when broth is called for in the other recipe selections in the VLCD and Maintenance sections.

Make your soup in batches so you will always have a supply and variety on hand. All the recipes in this chapter freeze very well. For convenience, you may wish to package them in exact portion sizes. For quick access to broth for use in other recipes, freeze by the tablespoon in ice trays and transfer to a zipper-locked bag.

Italian Chicken and Escarole Soup
(Recipe on page 23)

Basic Chicken Broth

Using pre-weighed boneless, skinless chicken breasts will eliminate any need for straining fat, while the resulting cooked portions can be readily used in recipes that call for boiled or poached chicken breasts.

4 3.5-oz. boneless, skinless chicken breasts
½ large onion, roughly chopped
1 large celery stalk with leaves, roughly chopped
1 garlic clove, roughly chopped

Small handful parsley sprigs
1 thyme sprig
1 bay leaf
8 cups water
Salt and pepper to taste

1. Place all ingredients in a large soup pot and bring just to a boil over high heat.
2. Reduce heat to a very low simmer and cook, covered with a lid, for 2½ hours.
3. Remove chicken breasts with tongs and set aside for later use.
4. Strain broth, discard vegetables and sprigs, and keep refrigerated or frozen if not using immediately.

Makes about 4 one-cup servings (15 calories)

Basic Beef Broth

Look for beef round cubes and trim off all visible fat, or purchase a bottom round roast and cut into 3.5-oz. slices before adding to soup pot.

4 3.5-oz. slices bottom round roast (or equivalent beef round cubes)
½ large onion, roughly chopped
1 large celery stalk with leaves, roughly chopped
1 medium tomato, roughly chopped
2 garlic cloves, roughly chopped

3-inch sprig rosemary
4 sprigs parsley
1 sprig thyme
1 bay leaf
8 cups water
1 Tbsp. Bragg Liquid Aminos
Salt and pepper to taste

1. Place all ingredients in a large soup pot and bring just to a boil over high heat.
2. Reduce heat to a very low simmer and cook, covered with a lid, for 2½ hours.
3. Remove beef pieces with tongs and set aside for later use.
4. Strain broth, discard vegetables, and keep refrigerated or frozen if not using immediately.

Makes about 4 one-cup servings (15 calories)

Basic Fish Broth

Uncooked shrimp shells and tails are ideal for this broth but you can also use lobster shells or bones from non-oily white fish. When buying fish for your entrées, ask your fishmonger for fresh shells and bones that might otherwise be discarded.

Shells and tails from 1 lb. raw shrimp
½ small onion, chopped
1 medium celery stalk with leaves, chopped
¼ fennel bulb with fronds, chopped

Small handful parsley sprigs
Small handful dill sprigs
1 bay leaf
5 cups water
Salt and pepper to taste

1. Place all ingredients in a medium soup pot and bring just to a boil over high heat.
2. Reduce heat to a very low simmer and cook, covered with a lid, for 1 hour.
3. Strain broth and keep refrigerated or frozen if not using immediately.

Makes about 4 one-cup servings (15 calories)

Basic Vegetable Broth

One of the best ways to make a flavorful vegetable broth is with saved vegetable trimmings from your cooking, adding just enough water to cover. If trimmings are not on hand, follow the easy recipe below.

1 large onion, roughly chopped
2 large celery stalks with leaves, roughly chopped
1 large tomato, roughly chopped
1 cup sliced white cabbage
1 cup roughly chopped greens such as chard, beet tops, or spinach
4 garlic cloves, roughly chopped

Large handful parsley sprigs
2 sprigs thyme
2 bay leaves
1 tsp. dried basil
1 tsp. marjoram
½ tsp. paprika
8 cups water
Salt and pepper to taste

1. Place all ingredients in a large soup pot and bring just to a boil over high heat.
2. Reduce heat to a very low simmer and cook, covered with a lid, for 2½ hours.
3. Strain broth, discard vegetables and sprigs, and keep refrigerated or frozen if not using immediately.

Makes about 4 one-cup servings (15 calories)

Italian Chicken and Escarole Soup

Oh so *buono*, this classic soup featuring the bold flavor of garlic and nutritious Italian greens makes for a satisfying lunch or dinner with a crunchy Grissini on the side. Stevia helps to balance the slight bitterness of the escarole and add another layer of subtle flavor.

1 cup water

6 drops Sweetleaf Stevia Lemon Drop

3 garlic cloves, minced

1 medium head escarole, trimmed, washed, and roughly chopped

Dash red pepper flakes

Salt to taste

4 cups Basic Chicken Broth (see page 21)

2 3.5-oz. boneless chicken breasts, cooked and diced

Fresh squeezed lemon juice (optional)

1. In a medium pot, combine the water and Stevia drops and bring to a boil over high heat.
2. Stir in the garlic, escarole, pepper flakes, and salt, reduce the heat to medium-low, and simmer until the greens are tender, about 20 minutes.
3. Add the broth and chicken, stir well to combine, and continue to cook over low heat for 5 minutes.
4. Taste for the addition of salt and serve immediately with a squeeze of fresh lemon juice, if using.

Makes 2 servings (150 calories; 1 protein, 1 vegetable)

Hot, Sweet, and Sour Chinese Soup

If you like both hot and sour and sweet and sour Chinese creations, you will love this delicious rendition that offers the best of both worlds. The addition of beef turns this into a hearty one dish meal.

4 cups Basic Beef Broth (see page 21)

1-inch piece fresh ginger, left unpeeled and thickly sliced

1 garlic clove, peeled and smashed

3 Tbsp. red wine vinegar

½ tsp. ground white pepper, or more to taste

4 cups thinly sliced Napa cabbage

1 Tbsp. Bragg Liquid Aminos

2 Tbsp. water

¼ tsp. Clear Stevia drops

2 3.5-oz. pieces cooked bottom round roast, cut into thin strips

Salt to taste

1. Place the broth in a medium saucepan and bring to a boil over high heat.
2. Stir in the ginger, garlic, vinegar, and pepper, reduce the heat to low, cover and simmer for 8 minutes, stirring occasionally.
3. Remove the ginger and garlic with a slotted spoon, stir in the cabbage, return to a simmer, and continue cooking, covered, until cabbage is tender, 5 to 8 minutes more.
4. Meanwhile, in a small bowl, mix together the Bragg Liquid Aminos, water, and Stevia. Marinate the strips of beef in the mixture, tossing well to coat, for at least 5 minutes.
5. Stir the beef and its marinade into the soup and continue to cook 2 minutes until heated through. Add salt to taste, if necessary, and serve immediately.

Makes 2 servings (220 calories; 1 protein, 1 vegetable)

Lemon Egg Drop Soup

This tangy Greek-inspired soup uses eggs as your protein, resulting in a light and soothing soup that's perfect for lunch. If you choose to add the spinach, it will count as one vegetable per serving.

2 cups Basic Chicken Broth (see page 21)

4 large eggs (use 1 whole and 3 whites)

Juice of ½ a lemon

2 to 4 drops Sweetleaf Stevia Lemon Drop

2 cups baby spinach (optional)

Salt and pepper to taste

1 Tbsp. finely chopped parsley

1. Place broth in a medium saucepan and bring to a simmer over medium heat.
2. In a small bowl, whisk together the eggs, lemon juice, and Stevia drops. Slowly whisk in about 1 cup of the hot broth and transfer bowl contents to the saucepan.
3. Add spinach, if using, and continue cooking over low heat for 5 to 8 minutes, stirring often.
4. Just before serving, season to taste with salt and pepper, and stir in the parsley.

Makes 1 serving (125 calories; ½ protein, 1 vegetable, lemon juice)

Fabulous French Onion Soup

Here's a tangy and terrific version of an old bistro favorite. Diced apple and Stevia add a hint of sweetness, while fresh thyme complements the flavors. Serve topped with breadstick pieces for a bit of crunch.

2 large onions, peeled, halved, and thinly sliced

Salt and pepper to taste

1 medium apple, cored and diced small

1 sprig fresh thyme

1 garlic clove, minced

2 Tbsp. red wine vinegar

$\frac{1}{8}$ tsp. Clear Stevia drops

4 cups Basic Beef Broth (see page 21)

1 tsp. chopped parsley (optional)

1. Heat a large nonstick skillet over medium-high heat. Add the onions, season with salt and pepper, and cook, stirring often, until soft and lightly browned, about 30 minutes. Reduce heat as necessary to prevent burning.
2. Add the apple and thyme, stir to combine, and continue to cook for 3 to 5 minutes. Add the garlic and cook 1 minute.
3. In a small bowl, combine the vinegar and Stevia and pour this into the skillet, stirring constantly. Transfer to a saucepan and add the broth to the onion mixture. Bring to simmer and allow to cook over low heat for 10 minutes, stirring occasionally.
4. Season to taste with salt and pepper and serve immediately, topped with a pinch of chopped parsley, if using.

Makes 2 servings (160 calories; 1 vegetable, ½ fruit)

Spicy Shrimp Curried Coconut Soup

Fans of Thai cuisine will be delighted with this easy-to-make, flavorful soup with a real kick, perfect as a protein selection when paired with a refreshing and crisp salad. You can make this as intensely hot as you like by substituting mild curry powder and paprika for the spicier versions.

7 oz. raw medium or large shrimp, shelled, tailed, and deveined

1½ tsp. hot curry powder

Dash of hot paprika

Salt and pepper to taste

3 cups Basic Fish Broth (see page 22)

1 cup water

1 tsp. peeled and finely chopped fresh ginger

15 drops Capella Coconut

¼ tsp. Clear Stevia drops

2 Tbsp. milk

2 tsp. chopped fresh cilantro

Dash Frank's Hot Sauce (optional)

1. Roughly chop the shrimp and place in a medium mixing bowl. Toss with ½ tsp. of the curry powder, the paprika, salt, and pepper, and set aside.
2. Combine the remaining curry powder, broth, water, ginger, Capella drops, and Stevia in a large saucepan. Bring to a boil over high heat then reduce to a simmer, stirring occasionally, and cook for 5 minutes.
3. Add the seasoned shrimp, stir well, and continue to cook at a low simmer until the shrimp is pink, about 4 minutes.
4. Stir in the milk and cilantro and taste for the addition of salt and pepper.
5. Serve with a dash of Frank's Hot Sauce, if using.

Makes 2 servings (125 calories; 1 protein, 1 milk)

Cream of Fennel Soup with Orange and Coriander

French cuisine has always relished the wonderfully aromatic qualities of fennel as a base for soup. Here, the anise-flavored vegetable teams up with sweet orange and piquant coriander for a super result.

3 cups Basic Chicken or Vegetable Broth (see pages 21 and 22)

1 cup water

2 medium oranges, peeled, seeded, and roughly chopped

8 drops Sweetleaf Stevia Valencia Orange

6 drops Capella Orange Creamsicle

1 Tbsp. coriander seeds

3 cups roughly chopped fennel, tough stalks removed

Salt and pepper to taste

Fennel fronds for garnish

1. Combine the broth, water, oranges, Stevia drops, and coriander seeds in a soup pot and bring to a boil over high heat.
2. Stir in the fennel, reduce the heat to low, cover, and cook until the fennel is fork tender, 20 to 25 minutes.
3. Transfer the mixture to a blender, working in batches if necessary, and puree until completely smooth.
4. Return to a clean saucepan, season to taste with salt and pepper, and serve immediately, garnished with fennel fronds.

Makes 2 servings (120 calories; 1 vegetable, 1 fruit)

Cool Minty Cucumber Soup

No cooking required for this refreshing cold soup perfect for a hot day. Aromatic and tangy, with a hint of lemon, it's the perfect accompaniment for spicy grilled chicken. Look for English cucumbers, which are mostly seedless with soft rinds.

3 cups Basic Chicken or Vegetable Broth (see pages 21 and 22)
1 cup water
10 drops Capella Cool Mint
5 drops Sweetleaf Stevia Lemon Drop
5 drops Clear Stevia

1 tsp. ground cumin
Juice of ½ a lemon
4 cups English cucumbers, roughly chopped
¼ cup fresh mint, roughly chopped
Salt and pepper to taste
2 Tbsp. diced cucumber for garnish

1. In a large bowl, combine the broth, water, Capella and Stevia drops, cumin, and lemon juice.
2. Stir in the cucumbers and mint and set aside for 15 minutes.
3. Working in batches, puree the cucumber mixture in a blender until smooth and transfer to a clean bowl. Season to taste with salt and pepper.
4. Serve chilled, garnished with the diced cucumber.

Makes 2 servings (60 calories; 1 vegetable, ¼ lemon)

SIDE & MAIN COURSE SALADS

CRISP, REFRESHING SALADS are the perfect companions for simply prepared protein selections and will enhance any meal with great flavor and taste. Whether vegetable based, or combined with fruit, these terrific and easy-to-prepare dishes will satisfy your yen for healthy and delicious food at its best.

Some salads can become a whole meal when combined with beef, chicken, or a variety of fish choices, and you'll find a number of great recipes for those as well. As usual, the abundant flavors of Stevia and Capella will contribute a real twist of unexpected flavor and keep your palate delighted and interested during this very low calorie phase.

Tangy Apple Slaw with Poppy Seeds
(Recipe on page 34)

Cucumber and Valencia Orange Salad

Crisp and refreshing, this quick salad makes a great accompaniment for grilled chicken or steak.

1 medium cucumber, peeled and sliced thin (about 2 cups)
1 orange, peeled and segmented
¼ cup apple cider vinegar

6 drops Sweetleaf Stevia Valencia Orange
Salt and pepper to taste
1 tsp. fresh parsley, finely chopped

1. Combine the cucumber and orange segments in a medium bowl.
2. In a small bowl, whisk together the vinegar and Stevia drops. Pour over the cucumber mixture, season with salt and pepper, add the parsley, and toss gently.
3. Refrigerate for 30 minutes before serving.

Makes 1 serving (110 calories; 1 vegetable, 1 fruit)

Cucumber Crunch with Mint and Cilantro

This refreshing side salad is a great accompaniment for a spicy grilled or baked chicken breast.

1 medium cucumber, peeled, seeded, and diced
Juice of ½ a lemon
1 Tbsp. apple cider vinegar
3 drops Capella Spearmint

6 to 8 drops Clear Stevia
Salt and pepper to taste
1 Tbsp. fresh mint, chopped
1 Tbsp. fresh cilantro, chopped

1. Place the cucumber in a medium bowl. In a small bowl, whisk together the remaining ingredients except for the mint and cilantro.
2. Pour over the cucumber, toss to coat, and place in the refrigerator for at least 1 hour, tossing occasionally.
3. Just before serving, stir in the fresh herbs.

Makes 1 serving (24 calories; 1 vegetable)

Sweet and Tangy Red Radish Salad

Radishes never tasted so good in this marinated salad that's perfect served alongside grilled steak or fish.

2 cups red radishes, trimmed and thinly sliced
Salt and pepper to taste
Dash onion salt

⅓ cup red wine vinegar
Juice of ½ a lemon
10 drops Capella Pomegranate
20 drops Clear Stevia

1. Place the radishes in a large mixing bowl. In a small mixing bowl, combine the remaining ingredients and pour over the radishes. Toss well to coat and refrigerate, occasionally stirring, a few hours or overnight.
2. Serve well chilled.

Makes 2 servings (25 calories; ½ vegetable, ½ lemon)

Tangy Apple Slaw with Poppy Seeds

Sweet and tangy with the fresh crunch of apple and cabbage, this coleslaw gets better the longer it sits.

2 cups cabbage, thinly shredded
1 apple, cored and cut into bite-size chunks
⅓ cup apple cider vinegar
1 Tbsp. lemon juice

5 drops Clear Stevia, or more to taste
4 drops Sweetleaf Stevia Lemon Drop
Salt and pepper to taste
⅛ tsp. poppy seeds

1. Combine the cabbage and apple in a medium bowl.
2. In a small bowl, whisk together the vinegar, lemon juice, Clear Stevia, and Lemon Drop. Pour over the cabbage mixture, season to taste with salt and pepper, add the poppy seeds, and stir gently to coat.
3. Refrigerate at least 1 hour, occasionally tossing, before serving.

Makes 1 serving (150 calories; 1 vegetable, 1 fruit)

Super Strawberry Spinach Salad

A perfect pair for a sweet and light salad, this salad gets a second burst of flavor from Stevia and Capella in this tasty combination.

3 cups fresh baby spinach
10 strawberries, stemmed and thinly sliced
⅓ cup apple cider vinegar

6 drops Sweetleaf Stevia Berry
4 drops Capella Sweet Strawberry
Salt and pepper to taste

1. Combine the spinach and strawberries in a salad bowl.
2. In a small bowl, whisk together the vinegar and Stevia and Capella. Pour over the salad and toss well to coat. Season with salt and pepper, and serve immediately.

Makes 1 serving (55 calories; 1 vegetable, 1 fruit)

Classic Spinach Salad

Ideal for a light lunch or supper, Stevia livens up the dressing with a hint of sweetness while Melba adds a bit of delightful crunch.

3 cups fresh baby spinach
⅓ cup red wine or apple cider vinegar
4 drops Clear Stevia
4 drops Sweetleaf Stevia Lemon Drop
¼ tsp. garlic salt

¼ tsp. dried oregano
¼ tsp. onion flakes
1 hard-boiled egg and 3 hard-boiled egg whites, peeled and sliced
Salt and pepper to taste
1 Melba toast, crumbled

1. Place the spinach in a salad bowl. In a small bowl, whisk together the vinegar, Clear Stevia, Lemon Drop, garlic salt, oregano, and onion flakes. Pour over the spinach and toss well to coat.
2. Arrange the egg decoratively on top of the spinach, sprinkle with salt and pepper, and finish with the crumbled Melba toast. Serve immediately.

Makes 1 serving (130 calories; 1 protein, 1 vegetable, 1 Melba)

Strawberry and Butter Leaf Salad with Hazelnut Dressing

Soft, buttery leaf lettuce is the base of this sweet and nutty salad that's a perfect accompaniment for grilled chicken.

2 cups butter leaf lettuce

10 strawberries, stemmed and halved

Juice of ½ a lemon

1 tsp. red wine vinegar

¼ tsp. minced onion flakes

5 drops Capella Hazelnut

6 drops Clear Stevia

Salt and pepper to taste

1. In a large bowl, toss together the lettuce and strawberries.
2. In a small bowl, whisk together the remaining ingredients and pour over the lettuce mixture. Toss to coat and serve immediately.

Makes 1 serving (60 calories; 1 vegetable, 1 fruit, ½ lemon)

Broiled Lobster, Grapefruit, and Endive Salad

Here's a gourmet dish that's sure to please with hints of sweet citrus, mint, and chives, all tossed together for a flavorful main course salad like no other.

3.5 oz. uncooked lobster tail meat

Salt and pepper to taste

½ grapefruit, peeled, and cut into bite-sized pieces, juices reserved

2 cups endive or chicory greens

2 tsp. chopped fresh mint

1 tsp. chopped chives

½ tsp. grated grapefruit zest

Juice of ½ a lemon

1 tsp. apple cider vinegar

3 drops Capella Cool Mint

9 drops Clear Stevia

1. Preheat the broiler to high. Place the lobster tail meat on a foil-covered baking sheet and season with salt and pepper. Sprinkle the reserved grapefruit juices over the tail and broil until cooked through, about 3 minutes per side.
2. In a large bowl, toss together the grapefruit pieces, endive, mint, chives, and a little salt and pepper. In a small bowl, whisk together the zest, lemon juice, vinegar, Capella, and Stevia.
3. Pour the dressing over the endive mixture and toss well to coat. Slice the lobster tail meat into medallions and gently toss into the salad. Serve immediately.

Makes 1 serving (175 calories; 1 protein, 1 vegetable, 1 fruit, ½ lemon)

Spicy Coconut Ceviche

Any type of firm white-fleshed fish will work nicely here in this delicious rendition of a popular Spanish cold fish salad.

3.5 oz. Chilean sea bass, lightly steamed and cooled
1 cup onion, thinly sliced
Juice of 1 lemon
Dash of Frank's Hot Sauce, or more to taste
6 drops Capella Coconut
5 drops Clear Stevia
¼ tsp. dried oregano
Salt and pepper to taste
2 tsp. parsley, chopped
1 tsp. cilantro, chopped

1. Carefully break the steamed fish into bite-sized pieces and place in a glass bowl. Add the sliced onions and gently toss together.
2. In a small bowl, whisk together the lemon juice, hot sauce, Capella and Stevia drops, oregano, salt, and pepper. Pour over the fish mixture, use rubber spatula to gently coat, and refrigerate for 1 to 2 hours.
3. Just before serving, stir in the parsley and cilantro.

Makes 1 serving (180 calories 1 protein, 1 vegetable, 1 lemon)

Sweet and Sour Crab Salad

Hints of fruity sweetness highlight this satisfying, hearty salad with aromatic fresh herbs and the crunch of Chinese cabbage.

2 cups Napa (Chinese) cabbage, shredded
3.5 oz. lump or king crab leg meat, picked over
½ tsp. fresh basil, chopped
½ tsp. fresh mint, chopped
½ tsp. fresh cilantro, chopped
Juice of ½ a lemon
2 tsp. apple cider vinegar
6 drops Sweetleaf Stevia Apricot Nectar
4 drops Sweetleaf Stevia Valencia Orange
Salt and pepper to taste
1 garlic clove, minced
Dash Frank's Hot Sauce (optional)

1. In a large bowl, combine the cabbage, crabmeat, and fresh herbs and toss gently.
2. In a small bowl, whisk together the remaining ingredients and pour over the cabbage mixture. Carefully toss with a rubber spatula to coat and refrigerate for 30 minutes before serving.

Makes 1 serving (150 calories; 1 protein, 1 vegetable, ½ lemon)

Crunchy Curried Chicken Salad

Mild curry flavors and sweet apple bring out the best in this delicious main course chicken salad that's sure to delight.

3.5 oz. chicken breast, cooked and diced

2 Tbsp. Basic Chicken Broth (see page 21)

1 Tbsp. milk

¼ tsp. mild curry powder

4 drops Capella Amaretto

4 drops Clear Stevia

Salt and pepper to taste

1 cup celery, diced

1 medium apple, cored and diced

1. Place the chicken in a medium bowl. In a small bowl, whisk together the broth, milk, curry powder, Capella and Stevia drops, salt, and pepper. Pour over the chicken, toss to coat, and set aside for 20 minutes.
2. Fold in the celery and apple, and serve immediately.

Makes 1 serving (225 calories; 1 protein, ½ vegetable, 1 fruit, 1 milk)

Tropical Chicken Salad

The wonderful flavor of piña colada brings this delicious salad to amazing tropical heights with refreshing and irresistible results.

3.5 oz. chicken breast, cooked and diced

½ grapefruit, peeled and cut into pieces, juices reserved

1 Tbsp. milk

2 Tbsp. water

5 drops Capella with Stevia Piña Colada

4 drops Clear Stevia

Salt to taste

Dash paprika

2 cups romaine lettuce, thinly sliced

¼ cup mint, roughly chopped

1. Place the chicken and grapefruit in a large bowl. In a small bowl, whisk together the grapefruit juice, milk, water, Capella, and Stevia. Pour over the chicken mixture and toss to coat. Sprinkle with salt and paprika, toss again and set aside for 20 minutes.
2. Add the lettuce and mint to the chicken mixture and toss well to combine. Serve immediately.

Makes 1 serving (190 calories; 1 protein, 1 vegetable, 1 fruit, 1 milk)

Strawberry and Chicken Salad with Sweet Basil

This combination of unexpected flavors will become a favorite dish whether served over lettuce or on its own with a side vegetable.

3.5 oz. chicken breast, cooked and cut into bite-sized pieces
Salt and pepper to taste
Juice of ½ a lemon
2 tsp. apple cider vinegar

9 drops Sweetleaf Stevia Berry
4 drops Capella Strawberries & Cream
10 strawberries, stemmed, roughly chopped
1 Tbsp. fresh basil, chopped

1. Place the chicken in a medium bowl and season with salt and pepper.
2. In a small bowl, whisk together the lemon juice, vinegar, and Stevia and Capella drops. Pour over the chicken and toss to coat.
3. Fold in the strawberries and basil, and serve immediately.

Makes 1 serving (150 calories; 1 protein, 1 fruit, ½ lemon)

Orange Beef and Asparagus Negimaki

This flavorful cold salad version of a Japanese favorite is perfect for lunch or dinner and can even be prepared a day ahead for convenience.

3.5 oz. beef tenderloin, cut into ¼-inch slices
¼ cup Japanese Ginger Soy Dressing (see page 45)
¼ cup fresh orange juice

6 drops Sweetleaf Stevia Valencia Orange
¼ tsp. orange zest
2 cups asparagus, cut into 2-inch pieces and cooked to crisp tender

1. Place the sliced beef in a shallow rimmed dish in a single layer. In a small bowl, whisk together the dressing, orange juice, Stevia, and orange zest. Pour over the beef and marinate in the refrigerator for at least 1 hour.
2. Heat a nonstick skillet or grill to high. Cook the beef slices to desired doneness, about 30 to 60 seconds per side, and place on a clean plate to cool.
3. Lay each beef slice flat on a work surface and place several pieces of the asparagus in the middle. Roll up and secure with a toothpick. Refrigerate until ready to eat.

Makes 1 serving (210 calories; 1 protein, 1 vegetable, ½ fruit)

Darn Good Deviled Eggs

Always a favorite at picnics and buffets, these devilishly good treats are both satisfying and flavorful. Pair with celery sticks and Melba for a complete meal.

8 hard-boiled eggs, peeled and halved	Pinch dry mustard
Salt and pepper to taste	¼ tsp. minced onion flakes
1 Tbsp. milk	Dash paprika
4 drops Sweetleaf Stevia Lemon Drop	½ tsp. parsley, finely chopped

1. Place 4 of the white halves with yolks in a small bowl and mash together with the back of a fork. Season with salt and pepper and set aside. Discard remaining yolks or reserve for other use. Place the remaining 12 empty white halves on a serving plate and set aside.
2. Stir the milk, Stevia, mustard, and onion flakes into the mashed mixture.
3. Place a small dollop of the yolk mixture in each of the 12 white halves and top each with a little paprika and chopped parsley. Cover and refrigerate until ready to eat.

Makes 2 servings (145 calories; 1 protein, ½ milk)

Minty Radish and Grapefruit Slaw

This delicious combination benefits from a touch of cool mint and sweet Stevia for a slaw that's perfect with simply grilled fish.

2 cups red radishes, trimmed and diced	6 drops Capella Cool Mint
	8 drops Clear Stevia
½ grapefruit, peeled, seeded, and chopped; reserve juice	Salt to taste
	1 Tbsp. chopped fresh mint leaves
Juice of ½ lemon	

1. Combine the radishes and grapefruit in a mixing bowl. In a small bowl whisk together the reserved grapefruit juice, lemon juice, Capella and Stevia.
2. Pour the dressing over the radish mixture, season with salt, and toss well to coat. Allow to refrigerate for 30 minutes before serving. Top with the chopped mint.

Makes 1 serving. (100 calories; 1 vegetable, 1 fruit, ½ lemon)

Tandoori Shrimp Salad

The flavors of India highlight this satisfying main course salad with hints of orange and cilantro.

3.5 oz. jumbo shrimp, peeled and deveined
Juice of ½ a lemon
8 drops Sweetleaf Stevia Valencia Orange
3 cardamom pods, crushed
1 large garlic clove, minced
1 Tbsp. fresh ginger, minced
1½ tsp. turmeric

1 tsp. paprika, hot or mild
Salt to taste
2 cups escarole or chicory greens
½ orange, peeled and segmented
Juice of ½ an orange
Freshly ground black pepper
1 tsp. chopped cilantro

1. Place the shrimp in a single layer in a shallow dish. In a small bowl, combine the lemon juice, Stevia, cardamom, garlic, ginger, turmeric, and paprika and pour over the shrimp. Allow to marinate in the refrigerator for 1 hour.
2. Heat a grill or broiler. Remove the shrimp from the marinade and season with salt. Grill or broil until pink and cooked through, about 3 minutes. Set aside.
2. In a large bowl, combine the escarole, orange segments, and juice, and add a pinch of salt and plenty of freshly ground pepper. Toss well to coat.
3. Transfer the greens to a serving dish and place the cooked shrimp on top. Sprinkle with the cilantro and serve.

Makes 1 serving (200 calories; 1 protein, 1 vegetable, 1 fruit, ½ lemon)

DRESSINGS, SAUCES, AND CONDIMENTS

LOW CALORIE AND INGREDIENT-RESTRICTED diets can naturally limit your use of tasty dressings, sauces, and condiments. Not so when Capella and Stevia are on board to help! Thanks to the variety of flavors available and the easy sweetening capabilities of a few drops, wonderfully delicious recipes for adding flavor and excitement to your meals are back on the menu.

When using any of these recipes in preparing or serving your meals, be sure to include the vegetable and fruit that they contain in your daily food count and stick to the rule of "no combining." In most cases, the recipe headnotes will give you ideas for how to serve these delectable dressings, sauces, and condiments while sticking to your allotted portions.

Oven-Roasted Tomato Ketchup
(Recipe on page 47)

Japanese Ginger Soy Dressing

Delicious Asian flavors combine in this terrific recipe that's great as a salad dressing, marinade, or sauce.

2 garlic cloves, minced
2 tsp. fresh ginger, minced
¼ tsp. powdered mustard
Juice of ½ a lemon
2 Tbsp. red wine vinegar

6 drops Sweetleaf Stevia Apricot Nectar
8 drops Clear Stevia
½ cup broth or water
⅓ cup Bragg Liquid Aminos
Salt and pepper to taste

In a small bowl, whisk together the garlic, ginger, mustard, and lemon juice. In another bowl, combine the remaining ingredients and slowly whisk into the garlic mixture. Taste for seasoning and store in an airtight container in the refrigerator for up to 1 week.

Makes about 1 cup

Very Berry Vinaigrette

The fruity and sweet flavors of Capella and Stevia make this a knockout dressing perfect for spinach or any leafy green salad.

10 strawberries, stemmed and quartered
Juice of ½ a lemon
¼ cup apple cider vinegar

4 drops Capella Strawberries & Cream
8 drops Sweetleaf Stevia Berry
5 drops Clear Stevia
Salt and pepper to taste

1. Place the strawberries in a bowl and set aside. In another bowl, combine the remaining ingredients and pour over the strawberries. Allow to marinate for 15 minutes, stirring occasionally.
2. Transfer the mixture to a blender and puree until smooth. Taste for seasoning and more Stevia, if desired, and store in an airtight container in the refrigerator for up to 3 days.

Makes 2 servings (25 calories; ½ fruit, ¼ lemon)

Strawberry Mint Dressing

Terrific on a dark green salad or as a sauce for baked fish, two delicious flavors come together in this easy-to-make dressing.

10 strawberries, stemmed and quartered
Juice of ½ a lemon
¼ cup apple cider vinegar

4 drops Capella Sweet Strawberry
2 drops Capella Spearmint
12 to 15 drops Clear Stevia
Salt and pepper to taste

1. Place half the strawberries in a bowl and set aside. In another bowl, combine the remaining strawberries and ingredients and marinate for 15 minutes, stirring occasionally.
2. Transfer the marinated mixture and liquid to a blender and puree until smooth. Roughly chop the strawberries that were set aside and stir into the blended mixture. Taste for seasoning and more Stevia, if desired, and store in an airtight container in the refrigerator for up to 3 days.

Makes 2 servings (25 calories; ½ fruit)

Orange and Hazelnut Citronette

Sweet and nutty, this dressing is great for salad or fruit and also makes a great sauce for simply grilled or baked chicken.

Juice of ½ an orange
2 Tbsp. apple cider vinegar
Salt and pepper to taste
¼ tsp. dried parsley
6 drops Sweetleaf Stevia Valencia Orange

Segments from ½ orange, roughly chopped
6 drops Capella Hazelnut
4 drops Clear Stevia
1 Melba toast, crumbled

1. In a small bowl, whisk together the orange juice, vinegar, salt, pepper, parsley, and Orange and Clear Stevia drops. Stir in the chopped orange and chill in the refrigerator until ready to use.
2. Meanwhile, combine the Hazelnut drops with the Melba crumbs, using your fingers to distribute the flavor.
3. When ready to serve, pour the citronette over salad or chicken, and top with the flavored Melba crumbs. Serve immediately.

Makes 2 servings (45 calories; ½ fruit, ½ Melba)

Oven-Roasted Tomato Ketchup

Roasting tomatoes brings out their natural sweetness and, with a little help from Stevia, everyone's favorite condiment is back on the menu.

4 medium tomatoes, cored and
    quartered
Salt and pepper to taste
2 garlic cloves, minced
1 Tbsp. onion flakes

¼ tsp. ground cinnamon
¼ tsp. allspice
¼ cup apple cider vinegar
15 drops Sweetleaf Stevia Grape
8 drops Clear Stevia

1. Preheat the oven to 350° F. Place the tomatoes on a nonstick baking sheet and sprinkle with salt and pepper.
2. Roast the tomatoes in the oven until softened, about 15 minutes. Carefully transfer to a blender and puree until smooth. Pour into a small saucepan.
3. Add the remaining ingredients to the saucepan, stir well, and cook over low heat until thickened, 20 to 25 minutes. Taste for the addition of salt or Stevia and set aside to cool. Keep refrigerated for up to 1 week.

Makes 4 servings (25 calories; 1 vegetable)

Zesty Steak Sauce

When a juicy, lean steak is on the menu, dazzle your taste buds with this perfect dipping sauce on the side. Great with grilled chicken, too.

2 tomatoes, cored, seeded, and
    chopped
2 Tbsp. red wine vinegar
2 Tbsp. Bragg Liquid Aminos
8 drops Capella Raspberry

15 drops Clear Stevia
½ tsp. garlic
½ tsp. onion powder
Frank's Hot Sauce to taste
Salt and pepper to taste

1. Combine all the ingredients in a medium saucepan and cook over medium-low heat, stirring often, until thick.
2. Using a handheld immersion blender or a regular blender, puree the sauce until smooth. Set aside to cool.
3. Taste for the addition of salt or Stevia, transfer to an airtight container, and keep refrigerated for up to 1 week.

Makes 4 servings (35 calories; ½ vegetable)

Smokehouse BBQ Sauce

This thick and rich sauce will spice up your chicken or shrimp with more flavor than anything out of a bottle!

4 medium tomatoes, cored and quartered	½ tsp. Bragg Liquid Aminos
Salt and pepper to taste	¼ cup apple cider vinegar
2 garlic cloves, minced	10 drops Capella Sizzlin' Bacon
1 Tbsp. onion flakes	⅛ tsp. Clear Stevia

1. Preheat the oven to 350° F. Place the tomatoes on a nonstick baking sheet and sprinkle with salt and pepper.
2. Roast the tomatoes in the oven until softened, about 15 minutes. Carefully transfer to a blender and puree until smooth. Pour into a small saucepan.
3. Add the remaining ingredients to the saucepan, stir well, and cook over low heat until thickened, 20 to 25 minutes. Taste for the addition of salt or Stevia and set aside to cool. Keep refrigerated for up to 1 week. Use to baste beef, chicken, or shrimp while grilling.

Makes about 4 servings (25 calories; 1 vegetable)

Thai Peanut Wet Rub

This nutty, flavorful wet rub will turn your grilled chicken, beef, or shrimp into an exotic feast!

2 garlic cloves, minced	½ tsp. onion powder
2 tsp. fresh ginger, minced	1 Tbsp. apple cider vinegar
¼ tsp. powdered mustard	1 tsp. Bragg Liquid Aminos
¼ tsp. salt	8 drops Capella Peanut Butter
Freshly ground pepper	12 drops Clear Stevia
Dash cayenne pepper	

In a small bowl, stir together all the ingredients with a fork to form a paste. Use immediately or store in an airtight container in the refrigerator for up to 1 week.

Makes about 2 servings (9 calories)

Strawberry Onion Chutney

This tangy and sweet condiment, perfect for livening up all types of simply prepared meat, chicken, and fish, is great to have on hand for fast meal fixing.

1 red onion, diced
1 tsp. fresh ginger, minced
Salt and pepper to taste
3 Tbsp. apple cider vinegar
¼ cup water
6 drops Sweetleaf Stevia Berry

4 drops Sweetleaf Stevia Cinnamon
6 drops Clear Stevia
Dash ground cardamom
Dash cayenne
20 strawberries, stemmed and quartered

1. In a medium saucepan, combine all the ingredients except the strawberries and cook over medium heat at a low simmer for 5 minutes.
2. Add half the strawberries, stir well to combine, and continue to cook on low until the berries break down and the mixture is thick, 8 to 10 minutes. Remove from the heat, stir in the remaining strawberries, and set aside to cool completely.
3. Taste for the addition of salt or Stevia and transfer to an airtight container to store in the refrigerator for up to 2 weeks.

Makes 4 servings (30 calories; ¼ vegetable, ¼ fruit)

Chunky Cinnamon Applesauce

Terrific served alongside chicken or veal, or great just on its own, this applesauce version gets an unusual cinnamon kick from Capella Hot Cinnamon Candy.

4 medium apples, peeled, cored, and cut into chunks
Juice of ½ a lemon
¼ cup water
8 drops Capella Apple Pie

8 drops Capella Hot Cinnamon Candy
15 drops Clear Stevia
Dash ground cinnamon

1. Place the apples in a medium saucepan. In a small bowl, combine the lemon juice, water, Capella, and Stevia. Add to the saucepan, stir well, and cook over medium heat, stirring often, until the apples break down and the mixture has thickened, 10 to 12 minutes.
2. Add the cinnamon and continue to cook a minute more. Remove from the heat and set aside to cool. Taste for the addition of Stevia, transfer to an airtight container, and keep refrigerated for up to 1 week.

Makes 4 servings (100 calories; 1 fruit)

Valencia Orange Spread

To satisfy a sweet craving spread on Melba, or as a topping for grilled fish or chicken, this easy-to-make, marmalade-like condiment will become a real favorite.

Juice of 2 oranges

1 orange, cut into supremes, pulp and seeds reserved

1 Tbsp. orange rind, white pith removed, thinly sliced

¼ cup water

10 drops Sweetleaf Stevia Valencia Orange

10 drops Clear Stevia

1. To prepare the supremes, cut the ends off the orange and place flat on a cutting board. Using a sharp knife, remove all the rind and white pith from the outside. Cut in between the membranes of the orange to release the supremes and transfer to a small bowl.
2. In a medium saucepan, combine the orange juice, orange supremes, orange rind, and water. Bring to a simmer over medium heat and cook for 2 minutes. Set aside.
3. Wrap the reserved pulp and seeds in a little cheesecloth and secure tightly. Submerge in the hot orange mixture and allow the entire contents of the saucepan to cool.
4. Remove the cheesecloth packet and squeeze the juices into the saucepan. Stir in the Stevia drops and taste for sweetness, adding more if desired. Transfer to an airtight container and keep refrigerated for up to 1 week.

Makes 6 servings (70 calories; ½ fruit)

CHICKEN ENTRÉES

ALTHOUGH CHICKEN IS ONE of the most versatile protein choices during this phase, finding new and interesting ways of cooking it, especially with the short list of vegetables and fruits, can be challenging. In this chapter, however, the challenge is met with delicious and tantalizing results with the help of Capella and Stevia.

From Asian to Italian, to some more unusual ethnic cuisines, all bases are covered with recipes that are also fast and easy to prepare. When you're using ground chicken, remember to buy ground chicken *breast*. If unsure whether your ground chicken is exclusively from the breast, ask your butcher department to grind some fresh for you.

Chicken and Asparagus with Peanut Sauce
(Recipe on page 57)

Stir-Fried Lemon Chicken with Chard

Slightly bitter chard pairs perfectly with this sweet lemon sauce and tender chicken pieces for a delicious and satisfying entrée.

3.5 oz. chicken breast, sliced into thin strips
Salt and pepper to taste
¼ tsp. onion powder
Juice of 1 lemon
½ cup Basic Chicken Broth (see page 21)
8 drops Sweetleaf Stevia Lemon Drop
2 cups chard, stems removed, leaves roughly chopped

1. Heat a nonstick skillet over medium-high heat. Season the chicken pieces with salt, pepper, and onion powder, add to the skillet, and cook until no longer pink, stirring often, about 3 minutes.
2. Combine the lemon juice, broth, and Stevia in a small bowl and pour over the chicken. Stir well, lower the heat, cover, and cook for 2 minutes.
3. Remove the lid, add the chard leaves, and cook, stirring constantly, until just wilted. Taste for the addition of salt and pepper, then serve immediately.

Makes 1 serving (140 calories; 1 protein, 1 vegetable, 1 lemon)

Greek Cinnamon Chicken

Fabulous flavors abound in this quickly prepared chicken stew with aromatic hints of the Mediterranean.

7 oz. boneless chicken breast, cut into bite-sized pieces
Salt and pepper to taste
2 medium tomatoes, cored, seeded, and diced
2 garlic cloves, minced
1 cup Basic Chicken Broth (see page 21)
5 drops Sweetleaf Stevia Cinnamon (or Capella Hot Cinnamon Candy for a spicier twist)
Dash ground cinnamon
¼ tsp. turmeric

1. Heat a nonstick skillet over medium-high heat. Season the chicken pieces with salt and pepper and lightly fry in the skillet until no longer pink on the outside, about 2 minutes. Add the tomatoes and garlic, stir to combine, and continue cooking for 2 minutes more.
2. Add the remaining ingredients, bring to a simmer, reduce to low, and cook covered until the chicken is cooked through and the sauce has thickened, about 15 minutes.
3. Taste for seasoning and serve immediately.

Makes 2 servings (150 calories; 1 protein, 1 vegetable)

Chicken Fajita Wraps

Mexican spices and a hint of lemon highlight these delightful wraps made with soft and sweet butter lettuce leaves.

3.5 oz. boneless chicken breast, cut into thin strips

Salt and pepper to taste

½ tsp. chili powder

½ tsp. ground cumin

½ tsp. Bragg Liquid Aminos

¼ cup Basic Chicken Broth (see page 21)

Juice of ½ a lemon

6 drops Sweetleaf Stevia Lemon Drop

1 tsp. cilantro, chopped

2 cups Boston or Butter Lettuce

Frank's Hot Sauce (optional)

1. Heat a nonstick skillet over medium-high heat. Season the chicken pieces with salt and pepper and add to the skillet. Sprinkle with the chili powder and cumin and stir constantly to cook through, about 4 minutes.
2. Combine the broth, lemon juice, and Stevia and pour into the skillet stirring to coat. Remove from the heat and stir in the cilantro.
3. Serve immediately, wrapped in the lettuce leaves, with a dash of hot sauce, if desired.

Makes 1 serving (135 calories; 1 protein, 1 vegetable, ½ lemon)

Sautéed Chicken Breast with Strawberry Compote

This unique combination of sweet strawberries and simply flavored chicken is as moist and delicious as it is easy to prepare.

10 strawberries, stemmed and quartered

Juice of ½ a lemon

5 drops Capella Sweet Strawberry

8 drops Clear Stevia

3.5 oz. boneless chicken breast

Salt and pepper to taste

½ cup Basic Chicken Broth (see page 21)

½ tsp. fresh tarragon, chopped

½ tsp. fresh mint, chopped

1. Place the strawberries in a medium bowl. Combine the lemon juice, Capella, and Stevia and pour over the berries. Stir well to coat and set aside for 20 minutes, stirring occasionally.
2. Heat a nonstick skillet over medium-high heat. Season chicken with salt and pepper and lightly brown in the skillet on both sides. Add the broth, reduce the heat to low, cover, and cook until the chicken is tender and moist, about 5 minutes. Add a little more broth if necessary to prevent sticking.
3. Add the strawberries, cover, and continue to cook until the berries begin to soften, about 2 minutes more. Remove from the heat and stir in the fresh herbs. Serve immediately.

Makes 1 serving (150 calories; 1 protein, 1 fruit, ½ lemon)

Apple Stuffed Chicken Breasts

Poultry and apples always make a great pair and in this terrific rendition, they get a little sweet help from the delightful addition of Capella Apple Pie.

For the Stuffing:

1 medium apple, cored and diced
1 cup celery, diced small
Salt and pepper to taste
½ cup water
1 tsp. lemon juice

6 drops Capella Apple Pie or Green Apple
10 drops Clear Stevia
2 breadsticks, crushed into crumbs

For the Chicken:

7 oz. chicken filets, pounded thin
½ cup Basic Chicken Broth (see page 21)
Dash ground cinnamon

1. In a nonstick skillet combine the apples, celery, salt, and pepper. In a small bowl, combine the water, lemon juice, Capella, and Stevia and pour over the apple mixture. Cook, stirring often, until the apples and celery begin to soften, 6 to 8 minutes. Remove from the heat, stir in the breadstick crumbs, and set aside to cool.
2. Preheat the oven to 350° F. Place the chicken filets on a sheet of waxed paper in a single layer; sprinkle with salt and pepper.
3. Distribute the stuffing mixture among the filets, placing in the center and pressing with your fingers to form a mound. Roll up each filet and secure with toothpicks. Place in a nonstick baking pan and pour the chicken broth over the filets. Sprinkle with cinnamon, cover with foil, and bake until the chicken is cooked through, 25 to 30 minutes.
4. Allow to rest for 5 minutes before removing the toothpicks and serving.

Makes 2 servings (210 calories; 1 protein, ½ vegetable, ½ fruit)

Chicken and Asparagus with Peanut Sauce

Here's a favorite sauce flavor made possible with delicious Capella Peanut Butter drops and a dash of creativity.

3.5 oz. boneless chicken breast, cut into thin strips
Salt and pepper to taste
½ tsp. fresh ginger, finely chopped
⅓ cup Basic Chicken Broth (see page 21)
2 tsp. Bragg Liquid Aminos

1 Tbsp. milk
8 drops Capella Peanut Butter
4 drops Capella Coconut
8 drops Clear Stevia
1 cup asparagus pieces, cooked to crisp tender
½ tsp. sesame seeds for garnish

1. Heat a nonstick skillet over medium-high heat. Season the chicken with salt and pepper and add to the skillet, stirring constantly, until chicken is no longer pink, about 2 minutes. Stir in the ginger and cook 1 minute.
2. In a small bowl, combine the broth, Bragg Liquid Aminos, milk, Capella, and Stevia and pour over the chicken, stirring well to coat. Add the asparagus, reduce the heat to low, and cook covered, until the chicken is cooked through and the asparagus is hot, about 2 minutes.
3. Just before serving, sprinkle with sesame seeds.

Makes 1 serving (165 calories; 1 protein, ½ vegetable, 1 milk)

Applewood Bacon Chicken Filet

Make this with your choice of side vegetable or slice and use it to top a lettuce or spinach salad for lunch.

3.5 oz. boneless chicken breast
¼ cup Basic Chicken Broth (see page 21)
5 drops Capella Sizzlin' Bacon
¼ tsp. onion powder

2 tsp. apple cider vinegar
Dash Bragg Liquid Aminos
Salt and pepper to taste
½ medium apple, cored and cut into ½-inch slices

1. Place the chicken in a shallow dish. In a small bowl, whisk together the remaining ingredients except for the apples and pour over the chicken. Turn the chicken to coat evenly and allow to marinate in the refrigerator for 1 hour.
2. Preheat a grill to medium high. Grill the chicken on both sides until no longer pink inside and an internal thermometer reaches 165° F, about 4 minutes per side. During the last 3 or 4 minutes, grill the apple slices to brown and partially cook.
3. Transfer the chicken to a clean plate and arrange the apples around. Serve immediately.

Makes 1 serving (150 calories; 1 protein, ½ fruit)

"Popcorn" Chicken

Buttery and crisp on top, you'll love these little morsels made from diced chicken breast that are great on their own or could top a green salad as well.

¼ cup low sodium chicken broth
5 drops Capella Butter flavor drops
3.5 oz (100 g) boneless chicken breast, cut into ½ inch dice

Salt and pepper to taste
1 Melba toast, crumbled
3 drops Capella Butter
⅛ teaspoon poultry seasoning

1. Heat the broth with the Capella drops in a medium nonstick skillet over medium heat. Season the diced chicken with salt and pepper and add to the skillet, Stir as the chicken cooks through, about 3 minutes. Transfer to a small broiler-safe baking dish and set aside.
2. Preheat an oven broiler to high. In a small bowl combine the melba, Capella drops and poultry seasoning and sprinkle evenly over the diced chicken. Place under the broiler until lightly golden, about 2 minutes and serve immediately.

Makes 1 serving. (140 calories; 1 protein, 1 Melba)

Tropical Oven "Fried" Chicken

A crisped coating and the sweet flavor of coconut and pineapple highlight this satisfying chicken entrée that's terrific with a crisp green salad. Perfect "fried" chicken pairs well with Cucumber and Valencia Orange Salad (see page 33).

1 breadstick, crushed into crumbs	2 Tbsp. water
¼ tsp. lemon zest	10 drops Capella with Stevia
½ tsp. onion flakes	Piña Colada
Dash garlic salt	3.5 oz. boneless chicken breast
1 Tbsp. milk	Salt and pepper to taste

1. In a shallow dish, combine the breadstick crumbs, lemon zest, onion flakes, and garlic salt and stir well to combine. Set aside.
2. Preheat the oven to 375° F. In another shallow dish, combine the milk, water, and Capella. Place the chicken in the milk mixture and allow it to absorb on both sides for 10 minutes.
3. Season the chicken with salt and pepper and place in the crumb mixture, pressing well to coat on all sides. Bake on a nonstick baking sheet until the internal temperature reads 165° F and the chicken is cooked through and crisp, 25 to 30 minutes. Serve immediately.

Makes 1 serving (145 calories; 1 protein, 1 breadstick, 1 milk)

Spicy Chicken Cacciatore

Here's a zesty and delicious take on an old favorite that's sure to satisfy and just might taste even better the next day.

2 medium tomatoes, cored, seeded, and diced

2 garlic cloves, minced

½ tsp. onion flakes

1 cup Basic Chicken Broth (see page 21)

2 tsp. apple cider vinegar

10 drops Sweetleaf Stevia Grape

¼ tsp. dried oregano

¼ tsp. dried basil

¼ tsp. dried parsley

1 bay leaf

Dash red pepper flakes

Salt and pepper to taste

7 oz. boneless chicken breasts, each cut horizontally into 2 pieces

1. In a large nonstick skillet, combine all the ingredients except for the chicken. Cook, stirring often, over medium heat until the tomatoes break down and the sauce has thickened.
2. Submerge the chicken pieces in the sauce, reduce the heat to low, and cook, covered, stirring occasionally, until the chicken is cooked through and the sauce is thick. Serve immediately.

Makes 2 servings (150 calories; 1 protein, 1 vegetable)

Chicken with Sautéed Greens

Capella bacon-flavor drops add just the right flavor for this easy-to-make, one-skillet dinner.

3.5 oz. chicken breast, diced
Salt and pepper to taste
⅔ cup Basic Chicken Broth (see page 21), divided

2 cups beet greens, chopped
5 drops Capella Sizzlin' Bacon
Dash Frank's Hot Sauce

1. Heat a large nonstick skillet over medium-high heat. Season the chicken with salt and pepper and add to the skillet, stirring until no longer pink, about 3 minutes. Add up to half the chicken broth to prevent sticking. Transfer the chicken to a clean dish and set aside.
2. Add the beet greens to the skillet, stir to wilt slightly for 1 minute, then add the remaining chicken broth mixed with the Capella drops. Stir well, cover, reduce the heat to low, and simmer until the greens are tender, about 5 minutes.
3. Remove the cover and return the chicken pieces to the pan, stirring to combine. Stir in hot sauce, taste for the addition of salt and pepper, and transfer to a plate. Serve immediately.

Makes 1 serving (150 calories; 1 protein, 1 vegetable)

Holiday Stuffed Chicken Breasts

A festive stuffing featuring the flavors of the holidays make this chicken entrée a real winner at the table.

For the Stuffing:

1 medium apple, cored and diced
1 cup celery, diced
Salt and pepper to taste
¼ cup water

6 drops Pumpkin Pie Spice
8 drops Clear Stevia
2 breadsticks, crushed into crumbs

For the Chicken:

2 3.5-oz. chicken breasts
½ cup Basic Chicken Broth (see page 21)
Dash ground cinnamon

1. In a nonstick skillet, combine the apples, celery, salt, and pepper. In a small bowl, combine the water, Capella, and Stevia; pour over the apple mixture. Cook, stirring often, until the apples and celery begin to soften, 6 to 8 minutes. Remove from the heat, stir in the breadstick crumbs, and set aside to cool.
2. Preheat the oven to 350° F. Place the chicken breasts on a cutting board and, with your knife parallel to the board, cut the breasts horizontally almost all the way through, leaving the two halves attached. Open like a book and sprinkle with salt and pepper.
3. Mound the stuffing on top of each open breast and fold over. Secure with toothpicks or string, and place in a nonstick baking pan, pouring the chicken broth over. Sprinkle with the cinnamon and additional salt and pepper, cover with foil, and bake until the chicken is cooked through, about 35 minutes, or an internal thermometer reaches 165° F.
4. Allow to rest for 5 minutes before removing the toothpicks and serving.

Makes 2 servings (186 calories; 1 protein, ¼ vegetable, ½ fruit)

Chicken with Orange and Fresh Basil

This delicious combination will become a favorite preparation with its intense orange flavor that's perfect with a side of simply steamed asparagus.

3.5 oz. chicken breast filets
Salt and pepper to taste
Juice of ½ an orange
½ cup Basic Chicken Broth (see page 21)
¼ tsp. orange zest

8 drops Sweetleaf Stevia Valencia Orange
½ orange with peel, sliced into circles
1 Tbsp. basil, cut into julienne strips

1. Heat a nonstick skillet over medium-high heat. Season the filets with salt and pepper and lightly brown on each side without cooking through. Transfer to a plate and set aside.
2. In a small bowl, combine the orange juice, broth, zest, and Stevia and pour into the skillet. Cook for 1 minute to reduce the liquid slightly. Return the chicken filets to the skillet, top each with the orange slices, and cook, covered, over low heat until the chicken is cooked through and the liquid has been nearly all absorbed.
3. Transfer to a serving dish, sprinkle with the fresh basil, and serve immediately.

Makes 1 serving (190 calories; 1 protein, 1 fruit)

Curried Chicken and Onions

Not too spicy with a hint of sweet coconut, this dish will please curry lovers everywhere.

7 oz. boneless chicken breast, cut into bite-sized pieces
Salt and pepper to taste
2 cups onions, thinly sliced
1 garlic clove, minced
1 tsp. fresh ginger, minced
1½ tsp. mild curry powder
¼ tsp. ground cumin
¼ tsp. turmeric

¼ tsp. paprika
⅛ tsp. ground coriander
⅛ tsp. cinnamon
1 cup Basic Chicken Broth (see page 21)
8 drops Capella Coconut
10 drops Clear Stevia
Lemon wedges for serving

1. Heat a nonstick skillet over medium-high heat. Season the chicken pieces with salt and pepper and quickly sauté in the hot pan until no longer pink. Add the onions and continue to cook, stirring often, for 2 minutes.
2. Stir in the garlic, ginger, curry powder, and remaining spices and cook for 1 minute. In a bowl, combine the broth, Capella, and Stevia and pour into the skillet, stirring well.
3. Reduce the heat to low and cook covered until the chicken is cooked through and the sauce has thickened, about 12 minutes. Taste for seasoning and serve immediately with a lemon wedge.

Makes 2 servings (190 calories; 1 protein, 1 vegetable, lemon wedge)

Best Sweet and Sour Chicken

This old Chinese favorite gets a great boost of sweetness thanks to Stevia and is perfectly delicious with the accompanying stir-fried Chinese cabbage.

7 oz. boneless chicken breast, cut into bite-sized pieces

Salt and pepper to taste

⅔ cup Basic Chicken Broth (see page 21)

⅓ cup apple cider vinegar

9 drops Sweetleaf Stevia Valencia Orange

9 drops Sweetleaf Stevia Lemon Drop

2 cups Napa (Chinese) cabbage, shredded

1 tsp. Frank's Hot Sauce

1. Heat a nonstick skillet over medium-high heat. Season the chicken pieces with salt and pepper and quickly sauté in the pan until no longer pink.
2. In a small bowl, combine the broth, vinegar, and Stevia drops and pour into the skillet. Reduce the heat to low and cook, covered, until the chicken is cooked through and the sauce has reduced, about 8 minutes.
3. Using a slotted spoon, remove the chicken from the skillet and place on a clean plate. Add the cabbage to the skillet, season with salt and pepper, add the hot sauce, and cook, stirring often, until the cabbage is just wilted.
4. Return the chicken to the skillet with its juices, stir well, and cook 1 minute. Serve immediately.

Makes 2 servings (135 calories; 1 protein, ½ vegetable)

Three Alarm Buffalo Tenders

For lovers of heat, this take on buffalo wings can't be beat. Serve with mouth-cooling celery sticks on the side!

3.5 oz. chicken tenders, white tendons removed	4 drops Sweetleaf Stevia Lemon Drop
Juice of ½ a lemon	6 drops Clear Stevia
3 Tbsp. Frank's Hot Sauce	1 breadstick, crushed into crumbs

1. Preheat the oven to 375° F. Line a baking sheet with foil.
2. In a shallow bowl, combine the lemon juice, hot sauce, and Stevia. Marinate the chicken tenders in the mixture, turning occasionally, for 30 minutes.
3. Dip the tenders in the breadstick crumbs, pressing firmly to adhere and place on the prepared baking sheet. Bake until the chicken is cooked through and the outside begins to brown, 25 to 30 minutes. Serve immediately.

Makes 1 serving (140 calories; 1 protein, 1 breadstick, ½ lemon)

Savory Sage and Apple Chicken Burgers

Slider-sized burgers are a real treat in this terrific dish that's perfect with Super Sautéed Onions (see page 106).

3.5 oz. ground chicken breast	½ medium apple, peeled and grated
Salt and pepper to taste	3 drops Capella Green Apple
½ tsp. dried rubbed sage	4 drops Clear Stevia
Pinch dried thyme	½ cup Basic Chicken Broth (see page 21)

1. In a medium bowl, combine the ground chicken, salt, pepper, sage, and thyme. In another bowl, combine the apple with the Capella and Stevia drops. Work the apple mixture into the chicken mixture and shape into slider-sized burgers.
2. Heat a nonstick skillet over medium-high heat. Fry the burgers in the skillet, adding a little broth as needed to prevent sticking, until nicely browned on the outside and cooked through on the inside, 6 to 8 minutes.
3. Transfer to a plate with any accumulated juices and serve immediately.

Makes 1 serving (165 calories; 1 protein, ½ fruit)

Chicken and Spinach Meatloaf

Moist and delicious, this terrific meatloaf is hearty and satisfying with a touch of garlic and just a hint of sweet apricot.

6 cups baby spinach
2 garlic cloves, minced
Salt and pepper to taste
14 oz. ground chicken breast
½ tsp. dry mustard
1 tsp. onion flakes

2 breadsticks, crushed into crumbs
¼ cup Basic Chicken Broth (see page 21)
1 Tbsp. Bragg Liquid Aminos
10 drops Sweetleaf Stevia Apricot Nectar

1. In a nonstick skillet over medium-high heat, cook the spinach and garlic with a little water until wilted. Season with salt and pepper and set aside to cool.
2. Preheat the oven to 350° F.
3. Transfer the spinach mixture to a cutting board and chop coarsely. Place in a large mixing bowl with the ground chicken, mustard, onion flakes, and breadstick crumbs and mix well with your hands. In a small bowl, combine the broth, liquid aminos, and Stevia; add to the chicken mixture, stirring well to combine.
4. Transfer to a nonstick loaf pan and pat down firmly and evenly. Cover with foil and bake until the internal temperature is 165° F, about 40 minutes. Remove from the oven and rest for 5 minutes before slicing and serving.

Makes 4 servings (130 calories; 1 protein, ½ vegetable, ½ breadstick)

Swedish-Style Chicken Meatballs

The delightful aroma and flavor of baking spices highlights this take on a classic meatball dish that's great served with steamed spinach or chard.

7 oz. ground chicken breast
Salt and pepper to taste
1 breadstick, crushed into crumbs
Dash ground nutmeg
Dash allspice

⅔ cup Basic Chicken Broth (see page 21)
2 Tbsp. milk
4 drops Capella Raspberry
8 drops Clear Stevia
1 tsp. fresh parsley, chopped

1. In a medium bowl, combine the ground chicken, salt, pepper, breadstick crumbs, nutmeg, and allspice. Mix well with your hands and shape into meatballs the size of walnuts.
2. Heat a nonstick skillet over medium-high heat and lightly brown the meatballs, adding a little broth to prevent sticking if necessary. Combine the remaining ingredients in a small bowl, except for the parsley, and pour into the skillet. Stir to coat, reduce the heat to low, and cook covered until the meatballs are cooked through and nicely glazed in the sauce.
3. Transfer to a serving plate, sprinkle with the parsley, and serve immediately.

Makes 2 servings (150 calories; 1 protein, ½ breadstick, 1 milk)

Chow Down Chicken Sausage Patties

Stack 'em up and enjoy these zesty sausage patties with a serving of Chunky Cinnamon Applesauce (see page 49) on the side.

1 medium fennel bulb, trimmed, cored, and diced small
Salt and pepper to taste
Dash ground sage
7 oz. ground chicken breast
¼ tsp. poultry seasoning
2 Tbsp. Basic Chicken Broth (see page 21)
5 drops Capella French Toast
6 drops Clear Stevia

1. Heat a nonstick skillet over medium-high heat. Add the fennel, season with salt and pepper, add the sage, and cook, stirring often, until softened, about 6 minutes. Add a little water to prevent sticking, if necessary. Set aside to cool.
2. In a medium bowl, combine the ground chicken, fennel mixture, and poultry seasoning. In a small bowl, combine the broth, Capella, and Stevia and mix into the chicken mixture. Shape the mixture into flat 2½-inch wide patties.
3. Heat a clean nonstick skillet over medium-high heat and fry the patties until golden on both sides, about 5 minutes in all. Serve immediately.

Makes 2 servings (135 calories; 1 protein, ½ vegetable)

Asian Chicken Roll Ups

These tasty treats are hard to resist, so double the filling and keep it on hand for another meal.

7 oz. ground chicken breast
Salt and pepper to taste
1 garlic clove, minced
½ tsp. fresh ginger, minced
3 Tbsp. Bragg Liquid Aminos
2 Tbsp. Basic Chicken Broth (see page 21)

3 drops Capella Orange Creamsicle
6 drops Sweetleaf Stevia Valencia Orange
Dash Frank's Hot Sauce
1 orange, peeled and sliced thinly
Whole radicchio lettuce leaves

1. Heat a nonstick skillet over medium-high heat. Add the ground chicken, season with salt and pepper, and cook until no longer pink, breaking up any clumps with a fork. Add the garlic and ginger and cook 1 minute.
2. In a small bowl, combine the Bragg Liquid Aminos, broth, Stevia, and hot sauce and pour over the chicken mixture, stirring well to combine. Reduce the heat to low and cook, covered, for 10 minutes, stirring occasionally. Remove from the heat.
3. To compose the roll ups, place an orange slice in the middle of a radicchio leaf, mound a spoonful of the chicken mixture on top, and carefully fold over to eat.

Makes 2 servings (170 calories; 1 protein, 1 vegetable, ½ fruit)

BEEF AND VEAL ENTRÉES

DELICIOUSLY PREPARED BEEF AND VEAL dishes can be particularly satisfying during this stage of the diet. But creating variety and interest can be a real challenge. In this chapter, the challenge is met with an assortment of tender, succulent preparations that will make your mouth water.

Flavor enhancers such as herbs and spices go a long way in creating the delicious results you are after. The flavors of Capella and Stevia add their own twist, too, in easy-to-make dishes such as stuffed cabbage and sautéed veal that will satisfy your cravings for hearty entrées. Some recipes are complete on their own with vegetables included, while others pair nicely with the wide selection of side and salad recipes presented in this book.

Nonna's Garlic Meatballs in Marinara Sauce
(Recipe on page 77)

Quick Chinese Orange Beef

Fast and easy to make, this tasty beef dish gets a double dose of intense orange from Stevia and orange zest and a delightful zing from red pepper flakes.

3.5 oz. lean beef, such as tenderloin, sliced thin
½ tsp. onion flakes
2 cups Napa (Chinese) cabbage, thinly sliced
½ cup Basic Beef Broth (see page 21)
1 Tbsp. Bragg Liquid Aminos
Juice of ½ an orange
½ tsp. orange zest
8 drops Sweetleaf Stevia Valencia Orange
Dash red pepper flakes
Salt and pepper to taste (sparingly)
Segments from ½ orange, for garnish

1. Heat a nonstick skillet over medium-high heat. Season the beef with salt, pepper, and onion flakes, add to the skillet, and cook, stirring often, until slightly browned but not cooked through. Transfer to a clean plate.
2. Add the cabbage to the skillet, season with salt and pepper, and cook, stirring, for 3 minutes.
3. Combine the remaining ingredients except the orange segments in a small bowl and pour into the skillet with the cabbage. Return the beef to the skillet, stir well, reduce heat to low, cover, and cook until vegetables are crisp tender and beef is cooked to desired doneness, about 3 minutes.
4. Taste for the addition of salt and pepper, transfer to a serving dish, and garnish with the orange segments.

Makes 1 serving (300 calories; 1 protein, 1 vegetable, 1 fruit)

Skewered Steak and Onions

A quick marinade and grilling brings out the fabulous flavor of this kebab-style entrée that's delicious with Strawberry Onion Chutney (see page 49).

3.5 oz. lean beef, such as tenderloin, cubed

1 onion, peeled and cut into chunks

¼ cup red wine vinegar

8 drops Sweetleaf Stevia Grape

¼ tsp. dried oregano

1 tsp. horseradish

Salt and pepper to taste

1. Place the cubed beef and onion chunks in a shallow dish. In a small bowl, whisk together the vinegar, Stevia, oregano, horseradish, salt, and pepper, and pour over the beef and onions. Marinate for 30 minutes, stirring occasionally.
2. Preheat a grill or broiler. Thread the beef and onions on a metal skewer and pat dry. Grill kebabs to desired doneness, about 4 minutes per side for rare, turning the skewers occasionally to cook evenly. Serve immediately.

Makes 1 serving (265 calories; 1 protein, 1 vegetable)

Pan-Seared Filet Mignon with Peppercorn Sauce

It doesn't get much better than a prime filet drizzled with a tantalizing peppercorn sauce. This may become your Saturday night splurge!

3.5 oz. filet mignon steak

Salt and pepper to taste

Dash garlic powder

2 tsp. mixed peppercorns, gently cracked

⅓ cup Basic Beef Broth (see page 21)

1 tsp. red wine vinegar

8 drops Clear Stevia

1. Heat a medium nonstick skillet over medium-high heat. Season the filet with salt, pepper, and the garlic powder. Place the filet in the hot skillet, press down, and cook until browned, about 3 minutes. Turn the filet over, press down, and cook another 3 minutes until browned. Remove from the pan and set aside.
2. Add the peppercorns to the hot skillet and stir for 1 minute. Add the remaining ingredients, reduce the heat to low, return the filet to the pan, cover, and cook to desired doneness, about 5 minutes for medium.
3. Transfer the filet and sauce to a dish and allow to rest 5 minutes before serving.

Makes 1 serving (210 calories; 1 protein)

Pan-Fried Filet with Irish Cream Sauce

Unbelievable but true—this delicious steak gets a finish of flavorful sauce thanks to Stevia and a touch of creativity.

3.5 oz. filet mignon steak
¼ tsp. coarse ground black pepper
Salt to taste
1 Tbsp. milk

3 Tbsp. water
5 drops Capella Irish Cream
5 drops Clear Stevia

1. Heat a nonstick skillet over high heat. Press the pepper into both sides of the steak and season with salt.
2. Sear and brown the steak on both sides, then reduce the heat to medium-low, cover, and cook to desired doneness, about 4 minutes per side for medium rare. Transfer the steak to a serving dish and set aside.
3. Combine the milk, water, Capella, and Stevia in a small bowl and pour into the still-hot skillet, scraping up any cooked bits with a wooden spoon. Pour sauce over the steak and serve immediately.

Makes 1 serving (200 calories; 1 protein, 1 milk)

Tuscan Bistecca with Lemon

Fresh rosemary and lemon make this popular steak preparation of Tuscany a real winner. Perfect when paired with garlic sautéed spinach.

3.5 oz. lean steak such as sirloin
Juice of ½ a lemon
4 drops Sweetleaf Stevia
    Lemon Drop

1 tsp. rosemary, finely chopped
1 tsp. parsley, finely chopped
Salt and pepper to taste

1. In a shallow dish, combine the lemon juice, Stevia, and herbs. Season the steak with salt and pepper and let rest in the lemon mixture for 30 minutes, turning over halfway through.
2. Prepare a grill or broiler. Cook the steak to desired doneness, about 5 minutes per side for medium-rare. Remove from grill and let rest for 4 minutes before serving with additional lemon juice, if desired.

Makes 1 serving (100 calories; 1 protein, ½ lemon)

Classic Chili Mole

Flavorful ground beef enhanced with Mexican spices and a traditional hint of chocolate makes for a terrific and flavorful entrée.

7 oz. lean ground beef
½ tsp. onion flakes
1 Tbsp. chili powder
1 tsp. paprika
½ tsp. cumin
Dash cayenne pepper

Pinch salt
1 cup Basic Beef Broth (see page 21)
2 medium tomatoes, cored, seeded, and diced
8 drops Capella Chocolate Fudge Brownie (*for a sweeter mole, use Sweetleaf Stevia Chocolate*)

1. In a large nonstick skillet over medium-high heat, brown the ground beef, using a fork to break up any clumps. Add the onion flakes, chili powder, paprika, cumin, cayenne, and salt, stir well to combine, and cook another minute.
2. In a medium bowl, combine the broth, tomatoes, and Stevia and pour the mixture into the skillet, stirring well to combine.
3. Cook over low heat, stirring often, until the liquid is mostly absorbed and the beef is flavorful, about 20 minutes. Taste for additional seasoning, and serve immediately.

Makes 2 servings (175 calories; 1 protein, 1 vegetable)

Persian-Style Meatballs

These delicious mini meatballs, flavored with curry, cinnamon, and apricot are the perfect accompaniment for Persian-Style Cabbage (see page 103).

7 oz. lean ground beef
Salt and pepper to taste
½ tsp. curry powder

Dash ground cinnamon
½ cup Basic Beef Broth (see page 21)
6 drops Sweetleaf Stevia Apricot Nectar

1. In a medium bowl, combine the beef, salt, pepper, curry, and cinnamon and form into 1-inch meatballs.
2. Fry the meatballs in a nonstick skillet until browned on the outside and cooked through, about 15 minutes.
3. In a small bowl, combine the broth and Stevia and pour into the skillet to deglaze the pan and make a light sauce. Serve immediately.

Makes 2 servings (145 calories; 1 protein)

Nonna's Garlic Meatballs in Marinara Sauce

These Italian-style meatballs would make any grandmother proud with their zesty garlic flavor cooked in a sweet marinara sauce.

For the Marinara Sauce:

2 medium tomatoes, cored, seeded, and diced
2 garlic cloves, minced
½ tsp. onion flakes
Salt and pepper to taste
¼ tsp. dried oregano
¼ tsp. dried basil
¼ tsp. dried parsley
½ cup Basic Beef Broth (see page 21)
8 drops Sweetleaf Stevia Grape
1 bay leaf

For the Meatballs:

7 oz. lean ground beef
2 garlic cloves, minced
Salt and pepper to taste
1 breadstick, made into crumbs
1 Tbsp. milk

1. In a medium saucepan, combine the tomatoes, garlic, onion flakes, salt, pepper, and dried herbs, and cook over medium heat for 2 minutes, stirring often.
2. In a small bowl, combine the broth and Stevia and add to the saucepan. Bring to a low simmer and cook, stirring occasionally, until the tomatoes have broken down, about 15 minutes, adding a little broth if necessary to prevent sticking.
3. Remove the bay leaf and transfer sauce to a blender (or use a handheld immersion blender) to puree until smooth, returning it to the pot.
4. In a medium bowl, combine the ground beef, garlic, salt, pepper, crumbs, and milk and mix well. Form into meatballs the size of walnuts and place in the saucepan with the sauce. Cook over very low heat, covered, occasionally moving the meatballs around in the sauce to coat, until cooked through, 20 to 25 minutes. Add a touch of broth or water to thin if desired. Serve immediately.

Makes 2 servings (190 calories; 1 protein, 1 vegetable, ½ breadstick, ½ milk)

Sweet and Sour Stuffed Cabbage

Here's a classic favorite with a tempting sauce that's sure to make for a hearty and satisfying dinner.

7 oz. lean ground beef
Salt and pepper to taste
1 tsp. onion flakes
½ tsp. garlic powder
1 breadstick, made into crumbs
6 large white cabbage leaves, blanched in boiling water to soften

¾ cup Basic Beef Broth (see page 21)
¼ cup apple cider vinegar
¼ tsp. paprika
10 drops Sweetleaf Stevia Grape
6 drops Clear Stevia

1. Preheat the oven to 350° F.
2. In a large nonstick skillet, brown the ground beef with the salt, pepper, onion flakes, and garlic powder, breaking up any clumps with a fork. Remove from the heat and stir in the breadstick crumbs.
3. Place the blanched cabbage on a flat surface and spoon the meat mixture in the middle of each, distributing between the leaves. Roll up by folding in the sides and then folding away from you to make a secure roll. Place snugly, seam-side down, in a baking dish.
4. In a small saucepan, combine the broth, vinegar, paprika, and Stevia and bring just to a simmer. Pour evenly over the cabbage rolls, cover with foil, and bake, basting often, until the cabbage is tender and most of the liquid has disappeared, about 40 minutes. Remove the foil during the final 10 minutes and continue to baste. Allow to rest for 15 minutes before serving.

Makes 2 servings (215 calories; 1 protein, 1 vegetable, ½ breadstick)

Beef Fajita Wraps

Mexican spices and a hint of lemon highlight these delightful wraps made with soft and sweet butter lettuce leaves.

3.5 oz. beef filet, cut into thin strips
Salt and pepper to taste
½ tsp. chili powder
½ tsp. ground cumin
½ tsp. Bragg Liquid Aminos
¼ cup Basic Beef Broth (see page 21)

Juice of ½ a lemon
6 drops Sweetleaf Stevia Lemon Drop
1 tsp. cilantro, chopped
Boston or Butter Lettuce (equal to 2 cups)
Frank's Hot Sauce (optional)

1. Heat a nonstick skillet over medium-high heat. Add beef to the skillet, sprinkle with the chili powder and cumin and stir constantly to cook through, about 4 minutes.
2. Combine the broth, lemon juice, and Stevia and pour into the skillet stirring to coat. Remove from the heat and stir in the cilantro.
3. Serve immediately, wrapped in the lettuce leaves, with a dash of hot sauce, if desired.

Makes 1 serving (195 calories; 1 protein, 1 vegetable, ½ lemon)

The Big Bodacious Burger

This amazing burger that's loaded with bursts of flavor is even tastier when served with Tangy Apple Slaw with Poppy Seeds (see page 34).

For the Burger:

3.5 oz. lean ground beef
Salt and pepper to taste
½ tsp. onion flakes
½ tsp. garlic flakes

¼ tsp. dried mustard
¼ tsp. dried thyme
Dash cayenne pepper

For the Sauce:

1 Tbsp. red wine vinegar
1 Tbsp. Basic Beef Broth (see page 21)

6 drops Sweetleaf Stevia Grape
2 tsp. Bragg Liquid Aminos

1. In a medium bowl, combine all the burger ingredients, mixing well with your hands. Shape into a burger and set aside.
2. Heat a nonstick skillet on high and brown the burger on both sides. Reduce the heat to low, cover, and cook to desired doneness, about 4 minutes per side for medium-well.
3. In a small bowl, combine the vinegar, broth, Stevia, and Bragg Liquid Aminos. Remove the lid from the skillet and pour the vinegar mixture over the burger and continue to cook as the liquid is absorbed, about 1 minute more. Transfer to a plate and serve immediately.

Makes 1 serving (150 calories; 1 protein)

Veal Stew with Orange and Saffron

The exotic flavor of saffron combines beautifully with intense orange in this tender and mouth-watering stew that's sure to become a favorite.

7 oz. veal cubes, trimmed of all fat
Salt and pepper to taste
1 cup Basic Beef Broth (see page 21)
Juice of 1 orange
2 garlic cloves, minced

6 drops Sweetleaf Stevia Valencia Orange
Pinch of saffron threads
1 bay leaf
2-inch piece fresh rosemary

1. Heat a nonstick skillet or heavy-bottomed pot over medium-high heat. Season the veal cubes with salt and pepper and brown on all sides, adding a little broth to prevent sticking.
2. Add the remaining ingredients, bring to a simmer, and cook covered on low, stirring occasionally, until the veal is fork tender, 1 to 1½ hours. Add a little more broth or water if sauce thickens too quickly.
3. Taste for seasoning, remove the bay leaf and rosemary sprig, and serve immediately.

Makes 2 servings (200 calories; 1 protein, ½ fruit)

Veal Scaloppini with Mock Marsala Sauce

This simply prepared take on a popular veal entrée will delight your taste buds with its heavenly sauce.

3.5 oz. veal scaloppini, pounded thin
Salt and pepper to taste
½ cup Basic Beef Broth (see page 21)
1 Tbsp. milk

6 drops Capella Vanilla Custard
4 drops Sweetleaf Stevia Lemon Drop
1 tsp. fresh parsley, chopped

1. Heat a nonstick skillet over medium-high heat. Season the veal with salt and pepper and cook quickly without browning, about 1 minute per side. Transfer to a plate.
2. Add the remaining ingredients except the parsley to the skillet and bring to a simmer. Return the veal with its juices to the pan and cook at a simmer, occasionally turning the scaloppini over to absorb the sauce, until no longer pink, 2 to 3 minutes.
3. Transfer the veal with the sauce to a clean plate, sprinkle with the parsley, and serve immediately.

Makes 1 serving (145 calories; 1 protein, 1 milk)

Maple Glazed Veal with Apples

Fast and easy to prepare, veal cooks in no time and is delicious with the sweet counterparts of maple and fruit.

3.5 oz. veal cutlets, pounded thin	Pinch dried thyme
Salt and pepper to taste	½ cup water
1 cup onions, thinly sliced	6 drops Capella French Toast
1 apple, cored and thinly sliced	6 drops Clear Stevia

1. Heat a nonstick skillet over medium-high heat. Season the cutlets with salt and pepper, and cook briefly, but not all the way through, about 1 minute per side. Transfer to a clean plate and set aside.
2. Add the onion to the skillet and cook, stirring often, until slightly softened, about 2 minutes. Add the apples and thyme and cook, stirring another minute.
3. Combine the water, Capella, and Stevia in a small bowl and pour over the apples and onions in the skillet. Return the veal to the pan with juices, reduce the heat to low, cover, and cook until apples are crisp tender and veal is no longer pink, about 3 minutes.
4. Transfer to a dish and serve immediately.

Makes 1 serving (280 calories; 1 protein, 1 vegetable, 1 fruit)

FISH AND SEAFOOD ENTRÉES

WITH THE TERRIFIC SELECTION of allowable fish and seafood in the low calorie phase, it will be hard to decide which delectable dish to make next! From flounder to lobster, you'll find numerous tantalizing and mouth-watering recipes that will both satisfy and delight the senses.

Package your fish in 3.5 ounce serving sizes to make your preparation quick and easy. Keep frozen filets and shellfish in the freezer until ready to use. Defrost in the refrigerator overnight for the best results. Use fresh fish the day of purchase to ensure optimal flavor and freshness.

For the fish filet recipes, you can use flounder, halibut, Chilean sea bass, and sole. Lobster, crab, crawfish, and shrimp are the allowed shellfish.

Sole with Strawberry Mint Salsa
(Recipe on page 90)

Citrus Thyme Crusted Fish

Delightful sweet citrus wakes up the flavor in this delicious baked fish with an herb and orange crumb topping. Serve with a crisp salad for the perfect complement.

3.5 oz. flounder or sole filets
Salt and pepper to taste
¼ cup purified water
1 tsp. lemon juice
4 drops Sweetleaf Stevia
  Lemon Drop

4 drops Sweetleaf Stevia
  Valencia Orange
1 Melba toast, crumbled
¼ tsp. orange rind, grated
¼ tsp. dried thyme

1. Preheat the oven to 350° F.
2. Line a shallow baking dish with foil and place the filets in the dish in a single layer. Season with salt and pepper.
3. Combine the water, lemon juice, Lemon Drop, and Valencia Orange in a measuring cup and pour evenly over the filets.
4. In a small bowl, stir together the crumbled Melba toast, orange rind, and thyme, season with salt and pepper, and sprinkle over the filets.
5. Bake until the fish flakes with a fork and the crust is slightly browned, about 20 minutes.
6. Transfer the filets with a spatula to a dish and serve immediately.

Makes 1 serving (115 calories; 1 protein, 1 Melba)

Oven-Roasted Fish with Fennel

Fennel and halibut are the perfect partners in this wonderfully flavorful dish with a hint of dill and the light, sweet taste of orange.

1 small to medium fennel bulb	3.5 oz. halibut filet
Juice of ½ an orange	¼ cup Basic Fish Broth (see page 22)
8 drops Sweetleaf Stevia Valencia Orange	¼ tsp. dried dill
Salt and pepper to taste	Segments from ½ orange

1. Trim the fennel of stalks, reserving the fronds. Cut the bulb in half through the core and remove the tough core with a sharp paring knife. Slice the remaining halves thinly and set aside.
2. Heat a large nonstick skillet over medium-high heat, add the orange juice and Stevia, and stir in the sliced fennel. Season with salt and pepper, cover and reduce the heat. Cook until the fennel is fork tender, stirring occasionally, about 12 minutes.
3. Preheat the oven to 400° F. Place the fish in a baking dish with a lid. Pour the broth over the fish, sprinkle with the dill, and season with salt and pepper.
4. Smother the fish with the prepared fennel mixture and top with the orange segments. Cover and roast in the oven until the fish is cooked through, about 15 minutes. Transfer to a plate, garnish with the fennel fronds, and serve immediately.

Makes 1 serving (220 calories; 1 protein, 1 vegetable, 1 fruit)

Teriyaki Sea Bass with Napa Cabbage

A quick marinade provides maximum flavor in this Asian-inspired entrée with a kick of hot pepper.

For the Marinade:

⅓ cup Bragg Liquid Aminos	1 tsp. fresh ginger, finely chopped
2 Tbsp. red wine vinegar	8 drops Clear Stevia
1 garlic clove, minced	6 drops Sweetleaf Stevia Lemon Drop

For the Fish:

3.5 oz. Chilean sea bass	2 cups Napa cabbage, shredded
½ cup Basic Fish Broth (see page 22) or water	¼ tsp. crushed red pepper flakes

1. Combine the marinade ingredients in a shallow bowl and stir well to combine. Place the fish in the marinade and allow it to absorb the flavors for 20 minutes, turning over halfway through.
2. Heat a nonstick skillet over high heat. Remove the fish from the bowl, reserving marinade, and sear in the pan on both sides until browned but not cooked through. Remove and set aside.
3. Add the broth to the hot pan and scrape up any browned cooking bits. Add the cabbage and the crushed pepper and cook, stirring often, for 5 minutes. Pour in the remaining marinade and stir to coat.
4. Place the fish on top of the cabbage, cover, reduce the heat to medium-low, and cook until the fish flakes and the cabbage is crisp tender. Serve immediately.

Makes 1 serving (160 calories; 1 protein, 1 vegetable)

Amaretto Baked Fish with Orange Zest

Any firm white-fleshed fish filet will do in this delicious amaretto-flavored entrée with "mock" almonds and a hint of orange.

For the Fish:

3.5 oz. firm white-fleshed fish	5 drops Capella Amaretto
Juice of ½ an orange	3 drops Clear Stevia
1 Tbsp. milk	Salt and pepper to taste

For the Topping:

1 Melba toast, broken into small pieces	3 drops Capella Amaretto
½ tsp. grated orange zest	Pinch salt
½ orange, peeled, seeded, and roughly chopped	1 tsp. parsley, finely chopped, for garnish

1. Preheat the oven to 375° F. Line a rimmed baking sheet with foil. Place the fish in the middle of the pan.
2. In a small bowl, combine the orange juice, milk, Capella, and Stevia and pour over the fish. Season with salt and pepper.
3. In another small bowl, combine the topping ingredients and sprinkle over the fish. Bake until the fish flakes with a fork and the topping is lightly golden, about 15 minutes. Sprinkle with the parsley and serve immediately.

Makes 1 serving (195 calories; 1 protein, 1 fruit, 1 Melba, 1 milk)

Apricot Soy Glazed Shrimp

Sweet apricot-flavored Stevia is just the ticket for this super flavorful skewered shrimp dish that's sure to satisfy.

3.5 oz. large shrimp, shelled and deveined

For the Glaze:

½ cup strongly brewed apricot-flavored herbal tea
10 drops Sweetleaf Stevia Apricot Nectar
5 drops Clear Stevia, or more to taste

⅓ cup Bragg Liquid Aminos
1 garlic clove, minced
1 Tbsp. fresh ginger, finely chopped

1. Make the glaze by combining all the ingredients in a small saucepan and simmering until slightly reduced and thickened, about 5 minutes. Set aside.
2. Thread the shrimp on bamboo or metal skewers. Prepare an indoor or outdoor grill with a nonstick rack.
3. Grill the shrimp, while brushing frequently with the glaze, until pink, about 2 minutes per side. Transfer skewers to a serving plate. Boil remaining glaze for 1 minute and pour over cooked shrimp. Serve immediately.

Makes 1 serving (120 calories; 1 protein)

Quick Coconut Curry Shrimp

The terrific combination of curry and sweet coconut highlights this easy entrée served with wilted baby spinach.

3.5 oz. large shrimp, shelled and deveined
Salt and pepper to taste
¼ tsp. mild curry powder

1 Tbsp. milk
3 drops Capella Coconut
3 drops Clear Stevia
1½ cups baby spinach

1. Heat a nonstick skillet over medium-high heat. Season the shrimp with salt, pepper, and the curry powder. Add to the skillet and cook until pink, about 2 minutes per side.
2. Combine the milk, Capella, and Stevia. Add to the skillet, and stir quickly to coat. Transfer the shrimp to a serving dish.
3. Add the spinach to the skillet and stir until wilted, about 1 minute. Season with salt and pepper and place on top of the cooked shrimp. Serve immediately.

Makes 1 serving (120 calories; 1 protein, ½ vegetable, 1 milk)

Buttery Skillet Shrimp Scampi

With all the buttery flavor and none of the guilt, you'll be making these scampi delights on a regular basis.

3.5 oz. uncooked jumbo shrimp, shelled and deveined

Salt and pepper to taste

¼ cup Basic Fish or Vegetable Broth (see page 22)

2 garlic cloves, minced

5 drops Capella Butter, or to taste

Dash paprika

1 tsp. fresh parsley, finely chopped

1. Season the shrimp with salt and pepper and set aside.
2. Heat the broth in a medium nonstick skillet over medium heat. Stir in the garlic and Capella and cook for 1 minute.
3. Add the seasoned shrimp, reduce the heat to low, and cover. Cook until the shrimp is firm and pink, 2 to 3 minutes. Transfer the mixture to a serving plate, add a dash of paprika, sprinkle with the parsley, and serve immediately.

Makes 1 serving (115 calories; 1 protein)

Sole with Strawberry Mint Salsa

This unusual combination that's also fast and easy will become a favorite entrée in no time. Perfect when served with a side of steamed asparagus or green salad.

3.5 oz. sole filet or other white-fleshed fish

Salt and pepper to taste

1 Tbsp. fresh mint, finely chopped

Juice of ½ a lemon

2 Tbsp. apple cider vinegar

4 drops Capella Cool Mint

8 drops Sweetleaf Stevia Berry

10 medium strawberries, stemmed and diced

1. Preheat an oven broiler to high. Line a baking sheet with foil and place fish in middle. Season with salt and pepper.
2. In a small bowl, combine the chopped mint, lemon juice, vinegar, Capella, and Stevia. Add the strawberries, toss to coat, and set aside.
3. Broil the fish until cooked and just flaking, about 5 minutes.
4. Transfer to a plate, spoon the strawberry mint salsa over the fish, and serve immediately.

Makes 1 serving (130 calories; 1 protein, 1 fruit, ½ lemon)

New Orleans BBQ Shrimp

The surprising addition of Capella Cola drops adds the perfect hint of flavor for this rendition of a popular spicy shrimp entrée.

3.5 oz. large shrimp, shelled and deveined

For the Sauce:

½ cup Basic Vegetable Broth (see page 22) or water
1 Tbsp. lemon juice
1 Tbsp. red wine vinegar
1 Tbsp. Worcestershire sauce
½ tsp. Frank's Hot Sauce
4 drops Capella Cola
8 drops Clear Stevia
½ tsp. liquid smoke
¼ tsp. ground ginger
¼ tsp. onion powder
¼ tsp. garlic powder
⅛ tsp. chili powder
⅛ tsp. paprika
⅛ tsp. curry powder
1 medium tomato, cored, seeded, and chopped
Salt and pepper to taste

1. In a small saucepan, combine all the sauce ingredients and bring to a boil over medium-high heat. Reduce the heat to low and cook, stirring often, until the tomatoes have broken down and the sauce is thick and rich. Taste for seasoning and set aside. *(Puree tomatoes in a blender for a creamier sauce.)*
2. Preheat the oven to 400° F. Place the shrimp in a shallow baking dish and pour the sauce evenly over them. Bake until bubbly and the shrimp is cooked through, about 12 minutes. Serve immediately.

Makes 1 serving (140 calories; 1 protein, 1 vegetable)

Shrimp with Sweet Marinara Sauce

Delightfully sweet and flavorful, this tomato-based sauce with Italian herbs and spices is perfect for succulent shrimp.

1 medium tomato, cored, seeded, and diced

⅔ cup Basic Vegetable Broth (see page 22) or water

1 garlic clove, minced

6 drops Sweetleaf Stevia Grape

½ tsp. onion flakes

¼ tsp. dried oregano

¼ tsp. dried basil

¼ tsp. dried parsley

Salt and pepper to taste

3.5 oz. large shrimp, shelled and deveined

1. In a medium saucepan, combine the tomato, broth, and garlic. Bring to a simmer over medium heat and stir well.
2. Add the Stevia, onion flakes, herbs, salt, and pepper, and continue to cook at a low simmer until the tomatoes have broken down and the sauce is thick.
3. Stir in the shrimp, reduce the heat to low, and cook, covered, until the shrimp are pink, about 5 minutes. Serve immediately.

Makes 1 serving (140 calories; 1 protein, 1 vegetable)

Shrimp with Sweet and Smoky Tomato Sauce

You'll love the layers of flavor in this tangy shrimp entrée thanks to Capella.

1 medium tomato, cored and chopped

¼ cup water

3 to 5 drops Capella Sizzlin' Bacon

8 drops Clear Stevia

½ tsp. onion flakes

¼ tsp. Bragg Liquid Aminos

Salt and pepper to taste

3.5 oz. raw medium shrimp, shelled, tailed, and deveined

1. In a medium saucepan, combine the tomato and water and bring to a simmer over medium-high heat. Add the remaining ingredients except the shrimp, stir well to combine, and allow to cook, covered, over low heat, just until the tomatoes begin to break down, about 3 minutes.
2. Stir in the shrimp, cover, and continue to cook over low heat until the shrimp turn pink and firm, about 2 minutes.
3. Transfer to a plate or bowl and serve immediately.

Makes 1 serving (130 calories; 1 protein, 1 vegetable)

Quick Crawfish Tomato Etouffee

Tangy and flavorful, this tomato-based version of a Bayou classic gets a hint of sweetness from Stevia and a load of flavor from creole spices.

1 medium tomato, cored, seeded, and diced
⅔ cup Basic Vegetable Broth (see page 22) or water
1 garlic clove, minced
6 drops Sweetleaf Stevia Grape

½ tsp. onion flakes
1 tsp. creole-style seasoning
Salt and pepper to taste
Frank's Hot Sauce to taste
3.5 oz. frozen crawfish tails, thawed

1. In a medium saucepan, combine the tomato, broth, and garlic. Bring to a simmer over medium heat and stir well.
2. Add the Stevia, onion flakes, seasoning salt, pepper, and Hot Sauce and continue to cook at a low simmer until the tomatoes have broken down and the sauce is thick.
3. Stir in the crawfish tails, reduce the heat to low, and cook, covered, until firm, about 5 minutes. Serve immediately.

Makes 1 serving (140 calories; 1 protein, 1 vegetable)

Petit Baked Crab Cakes

These scrumptious two-bite crab delights are great for making in batches ahead of time for freezing and reheating.

7 oz. lump crab meat, picked over for cartilage and shells
½ tsp. Old Bay Seasoning
Pinch salt
2 tsp. fresh cilantro, finely chopped
2 tsp. fresh parsley, finely chopped

Juice of ½ a lemon
6 drops Sweetleaf Stevia Lemon Drop
2 Tbsp. milk
2 breadsticks, processed into fine crumbs

1. Preheat the oven to 350° F.
2. In a medium bowl, combine the crab, Old Bay, salt, and herbs and stir gently. In a small bowl, combine the lemon juice, Stevia, and milk. Stir into the crab mixture. Fold in the breadstick crumbs.
3. Form small balls and place in a mini muffin tin, gently flattening the tops. Bake until golden and hot, 15 to 20 minutes. Carefully remove from the tin and serve immediately, or cool and freeze in an airtight container.

Makes 2 servings (125 calories; 1 protein, 1 breadstick, 1 milk, ¼ lemon)

Spanish-Style Crab Stew

Here's a spicy way to enjoy crab with the flavor of bold garlic and a hint of citrus.

2 medium tomatoes, cored, seeded, and diced
2 garlic cloves, minced
1 cup Basic Fish Broth (see page 22) or water
Juice of ½ an orange
8 drops Sweetleaf Stevia Valencia Orange
½ tsp. dried oregano
½ tsp. Frank's Hot Sauce, or more to taste
Salt and pepper to taste
1 Tbsp. fresh cilantro, chopped
7 oz. lump crab meat, picked over for cartilage and shells
½ orange, cut into wedges

1. In a medium saucepan, combine the tomatoes, garlic, broth, orange juice, Stevia, oregano, hot sauce, salt, and pepper. Bring to a simmer over medium-high heat, stirring often. Reduce heat to low and cook until thickened, about 12 minutes.
2. Stir in the cilantro and crab, return to a simmer, cover, and cook on low another 5 minutes.
3. Before serving, taste for seasoning. Spoon into a bowl and serve with the orange wedges.

Makes 2 servings (160 calories; 1 protein, 1 vegetable, ½ fruit)

Crab and Onion Kerala Curry

This unusual curry comes from the fishing area of India and is bursting with flavor and fiery heat.

2 medium onions, peeled, halved, and sliced (about 2 cups)

2 garlic cloves, minced

2 tsp. fresh ginger, chopped

½ tsp. mustard seeds

½ tsp. coriander seeds

Pinch salt

Dash crushed red pepper flakes, to taste

1 tsp. hot or mild curry powder

⅔ cup Basic Fish Broth (see page 22) or water

2 Tbsp. milk

6 drops Capella Coconut

8 drops Sweetleaf Stevia Vanilla Crème

7 oz. lump crab meat, picked over for cartilage and shells

1 tsp. lemon juice

1. Combine the onion, garlic, ginger, mustard seeds, coriander seeds, red pepper flakes, and salt in a nonstick skillet over medium-high heat. Cook, stirring often, while seeds pop and onion begins to brown. Add the curry powder and cook 1 minute. Pour a little of the broth in to prevent sticking, if necessary.
2. In a small bowl, combine the broth, milk, Capella, and Stevia and pour into the onion mixture. Reduce the heat to low, stir to coat, cover, and cook until the onions have softened, about 8 minutes.
3. Stir in the crab, cover again, and allow to cook on low for 3 minutes more.
4. Just before serving, taste for seasoning and stir in the lemon juice.

Makes 2 servings (175 calories; 1 protein, 1 vegetable, 1 milk)

Poached Lobster with Strawberry Vanilla Cream Sauce

You'll think you've landed in a gourmet French café after one taste of this amazing dish that will have you rethinking strawberries and cream in no time!

For the Sauce:

10 medium strawberries, stemmed and pureed
1 tsp. fresh ginger, minced
1 Tbsp. red wine vinegar
Pinch salt

1 Tbsp. milk
3 drops Capella Strawberries & Cream
4 drops Sweetleaf Stevia Vanilla Crème

For the Lobster:

3.5 oz. lobster tail, uncooked
1 cup Basic Vegetable Broth (see page 22) or water

1 bay leaf
1 tsp. fresh mint, chopped

1. Make the sauce by combining the pureed strawberries, ginger, vinegar, and salt in a small saucepan. Bring to a simmer over medium heat, stirring often, and cook for 3 minutes until fragrant. Set aside.
2. In a small bowl, combine the milk, Capella, and Stevia. Stir into the strawberry mixture and keep warm.
3. Meanwhile poach the lobster tail in a small saucepan with the broth and bay leaf until pink and cooked through, about 8 minutes. Remove from liquid and pat dry.
4. To serve, pour the sauce on a rimmed plate, slice the lobster tail and arrange on top, sprinkling with the mint.

Makes 1 serving (150 calories; 1 protein, 1 fruit, 1 milk)

Broiled Lobster Tail with Sweet Lemon Butter and Tarragon

Simply broiled and napped with a light sauce, this lobster entrée will please the palate. Delicious served with sautéed spinach.

3.5 oz. lobster tail, uncooked
Salt and pepper to taste
Dash paprika
Juice of ½ a lemon

8 drops Sweetleaf Stevia Lemon Drop
5 to 6 drops Capella Butter
½ tsp. fresh tarragon, finely chopped

1. Preheat the broiler to high.
2. Halve the lobster tail lengthwise. Season with salt and pepper and add the paprika. Broil until pink and cooked through, 5 to 10 minutes.
3. Meanwhile, in a small bowl, combine the lemon juice, Stevia, Capella, and tarragon.
4. Just before serving, spoon the lemon mixture over the lobster.

Makes 1 serving (100 calories; 1 protein, ½ lemon)

Quick Lobster Stir-Fry with Spring Onions

Fast and flavorful, try this method with shrimp and firm white-fleshed fish filets, too.

3.5 oz. lobster tail meat, uncooked and sliced
1 cup spring onions, trimmed and roughly chopped
1 garlic clove, minced
1 tsp. fresh gingerroot, chopped

2 Tbsp. Bragg Liquid Aminos
8 drops Sweetleaf Stevia Valencia Orange
2 tsp. apple cider vinegar
Juice of ½ an orange

1. Heat a nonstick skillet over high heat. Add the lobster, season with salt and pepper, and cook, stirring constantly, until pink, about 2 minutes. Remove and set aside.
2. Add the spring onions, garlic, and ginger to the skillet, and stir-fry until onions begin to wither. Add a little water, if necessary, to prevent sticking.
3. In a small bowl, combine the liquid aminos, Stevia, and vinegar. Pour over the onion mixture, return the lobster to the skillet, and stir well. Pour in the orange juice, cover, and cook over low for 2 minutes. Serve immediately.

Makes 1 serving (190 calories; 1 protein, 1 vegetable, ½ fruit)

SIDE AND VEGETARIAN DISHES

THE **VLCD** VEGETABLES lend themselves to any number of delicious preparations. Here you'll find many wonderful ways to quickly prepare them with the assistance of Capella and Stevia flavors. From asparagus to spinach, the possibilities are endless, but you'll no doubt find a few that will become your favorites.

When using meat-based broth in any of the recipes that follow, remember to pair the vegetable recipe with the same type of protein at mealtime. If you're making a dish ahead of time and are in doubt as to what protein you'll choose, you can substitute the vegetable broth when chicken or beef broth is called for.

Vegetarians following the low calorie protocol of this phase have more delicious ideas than they may think! From hearty omelets to soy-based chili, the delectable entrées are numerous and varied.

Vegetarians will also find enticing meal ideas in this chapter using the protein serving of 1 whole egg and 3 whites, or a ½ cup portion of nonfat cottage cheese, as well as soy patties. When purchasing patties, stick with those that do not exceed 110 calories per serving and opt for the plainest and least seasoned, so as not to interfere with the flavors of the recipes.

Oven-Roasted Fennel with Fresh Herbs
(Recipe on page 105)

Side Dishes

Lemon Buttery Sautéed Asparagus with Crumb Topping

Asparagus never tasted so good in this easy-to-make flavorful recipe with a satisfying and crunchy finish.

For the Asparagus:
2 cups raw asparagus, cut into pieces
½ cup Basic Chicken or Vegetable Broth (see page 21 or 22)
5 drops Capella Butter
1 tsp. lemon juice

For the Topping:
Salt and pepper to taste
1 breadstick, crumbled
¼ tsp. grated lemon rind
3 drops Capella Butter

1. Place the asparagus in a large nonstick skillet. In a small bowl, combine the broth, Capella, and lemon juice. Pour over the asparagus and, over medium heat, bring to a simmer. Cover, reduce the heat to low, and cook until the asparagus is fork tender, about 5 minutes.
2. Meanwhile, make the topping by combining all the ingredients in a small pan. Cook, stirring constantly, over medium-low heat until heated through and slightly toasted, about 2 minutes. Set aside.
3. When the asparagus is cooked, remove the lid and transfer to a serving platter. Sprinkle the crumb topping over and serve immediately.

Makes 1 serving (84 calories; 1 vegetable, 1 breadstick)

Orange-Glazed Asparagus

Tangy orange adds a light and delightful glaze to asparagus that's perfect as a side dish for chicken, fish, or steak.

⅓ cup Basic Chicken Broth (see page 21)
Juice of ½ an orange
½ orange, peeled, seeded, and roughly chopped
5 drops Capella Orange Creamsicle
¼ tsp. orange zest
8 to 10 asparagus spears (about 2 cups), cooked to fork tender
Salt and pepper to taste

1. In a nonstick skillet, combine the broth, orange juice, orange pieces, Stevia, and orange zest and bring to a simmer over medium-high heat. Allow to cook on low and reduce by half.
2. Add the cooked asparagus spears, season with salt and pepper, and swirl around in the pan sauce until lightly glazed and heated through. Serve immediately.

Makes 1 serving (135 calories; 1 vegetable, 1 fruit)

Sesame Soy Stir-Fried Asparagus

Bursting with Asian flavors, asparagus never tasted so good! Great as a side dish for any teriyaki-flavored or simply prepared entrée.

½ tsp. sesame seeds
½ cup Basic Chicken Broth (see page 21)
2 cups asparagus, cut into 2-inch pieces

Salt and pepper to taste
1 tsp. fresh ginger, chopped
¼ cup Bragg Liquid Aminos
Juice of ½ a lemon
8 drops Sweetleaf Stevia Lemon Drop

1. Place the sesame seeds in a large nonstick skillet over medium-high heat. Stir as they begin to toast and cook until lightly browned, about 2 minutes.
2. Remove from the heat and pour in the broth. Add the asparagus, salt, pepper, and ginger. Stir well to coat, and cook, covered, over medium-low heat until the asparagus is nearly fork tender, about 4 minutes.
3. In a small bowl, combine the liquid aminos, lemon juice, and Stevia, and pour over the asparagus mixture. Stir well to coat and continue to cook uncovered until the asparagus is tender and the liquid is reduced. Serve immediately.

Makes 1 serving (100 calories; 1 vegetable, ½ lemon)

Sweet Braised Red Cabbage

Both sweet and a bit sour, this terrific side dish can be made in batches and is a great accompaniment for simply cooked veal or beef.

4 cups red cabbage, shredded
1 cup Basic Beef Broth (see page 21)
½ cup apple cider vinegar
5 drops Sweetleaf Stevia Berry
10 drops Clear Stevia

2 medium apples, cored and diced
¼ tsp. caraway seeds
2 tsp. fresh dill, chopped

1. Place the cabbage in a large pot. In a small pot, combine the broth, vinegar, and Stevia. Bring to a boil and pour over the cabbage.
2. Cook the cabbage at a low simmer, stirring often, for 10 minutes. Stir in the apple and cook a further 10 to 15 minutes until the cabbage is tender and most of the liquid has disappeared.
3. Remove from the heat, stir in the caraway seeds and dill, and serve immediately.

Makes 2 servings (165 calories; 1 vegetable, 1 fruit)

Persian-Style Cabbage

The secret ingredient is cinnamon in this fabulous side dish that's delicious with Persian-Style Meatballs (see page 76).

4 cups white cabbage, shredded
1 cup Basic Chicken Broth (see page 21)
8 drops Sweetleaf Stevia Cinnamon

Salt and pepper to taste
Dash ground cinnamon
Dash allspice

1. Place the cabbage in a large pot. In a small pot, heat the broth with the Stevia. Pour half the broth mixture over the cabbage, season with salt and pepper, and cook over medium-low heat, stirring often, until lightly golden, about 15 minutes. Add more of the broth mixture to prevent sticking.
2. When cabbage is cooked down to about $\frac{1}{3}$ volume and is nearly tender, stir in the cinnamon and allspice. Continue to cook a few minutes more until softened. Serve immediately.

Makes 2 servings (55 calories; 1 vegetable)

Scalloped Celery and Strawberry Crisp

The terrific combination of these unusual partners makes a delicious side dish for any type of simply prepared fish entrée.

2 cups celery, peeled and cut into ½-inch pieces
10 strawberries, stemmed and quartered
½ cup Basic Vegetable Broth (see page 22)

8 drops Sweetleaf Stevia Berry
4 drops Sweetleaf Stevia Valencia Orange
1 breadstick, crumbled

1. Preheat the oven to 350° F. Combine the celery and strawberries in a medium-sized ceramic baking dish.
2. In a small saucepan, heat together the broth and Stevia. Pour over the celery mixture. Cover with a lid or foil, and bake until bubbly, but the celery is still crisp, about 15 minutes.
3. Remove the foil, sprinkle the breadstick crumbs on top, and continue to bake until the celery is softened and the crumbs are lightly golden, about 15 minutes more. Remove from oven and allow to cool 5 minutes before serving.

Makes 1 serving (90 calories; 1 vegetable, 1 fruit, 1 breadstick)

Sautéed Lemon Garlic Rainbow Chard

Colorful rainbow chard is quickly prepared in this flavorful side dish that's perfect with any meal. Try using spinach, escarole, or beet greens in this recipe on other occasions.

½ cup Basic Chicken Broth (see page 21)
2 garlic cloves, minced
Juice of ½ a lemon
6 drops Sweetleaf Stevia Lemon Drop

4 drops Sweetleaf Stevia Grape
2 cups rainbow chard, stems removed, leaves sliced
Salt and pepper to taste

1. Heat the broth in a large nonstick skillet. Add the garlic and allow to simmer for 2 minutes.
2. Stir in the lemon juice and Stevia. Add the chard, season with salt and pepper, and stir to coat. Cover and cook on low for 12 to 15 minutes, until the leaves are tender. Serve immediately.

Makes 1 serving (35 calories; 1 vegetable, ½ lemon)

French Creole-Style Chard

Spicy and bold with a hint of maple, these greens will surely satisfy as a terrific side for chicken of any type.

4 cups chard, stems removed, leaves roughly chopped
½ cup Basic Chicken Broth (see page 21)
4 drops Capella French Toast

8 drops Clear Stevia
Pinch salt
¼ tsp. garlic powder
Dash cayenne pepper, or more to taste

1. Place the chard in a large pot. In a small bowl, combine the broth, Capella, and Stevia. Pour over the chard and bring to a simmer.
2. Stir in the salt, garlic powder, and cayenne, and cook, covered, until the chard is tender, stirring occasionally, about 15 minutes. Taste for additional seasoning and serve immediately.

Makes 2 servings (25 calories; 1 vegetable)

Cucumber Cilantro Salsa

Try this alongside grilled fish or chicken for a lively accompaniment that's full of great flavor and tang.

2 cups cucumber, peeled, seeded, and diced
Salt and pepper to taste
2 Tbsp. fresh cilantro, chopped

2 Tbsp. red wine vinegar
6 to 8 drops Capella Lemon Lime
8 drops Clear Stevia
Dash Frank's Hot Sauce

1. In a medium bowl, combine the cucumber, salt, pepper, and cilantro and toss well to combine.
2. In a small bowl, stir together the remaining ingredients and pour over the cucumber mixture. Toss again to coat well and refrigerate for at least one hour before serving.

Makes 2 servings (20 calories; ½ vegetable)

Oven-Roasted Fennel with Fresh Herbs

Fennel is just as delicious—if not more so, cooked as it is raw, and here it gets extra flavor from roasting and finishing with herbs and citrus.

1 medium fennel bulb, tough stems removed, fronds reserved
½ to 1 cup Basic Chicken Broth (see page 21)
Salt and pepper to taste
Juice of ½ a lemon
Juice of ½ an orange

4 drops Sweetleaf Stevia Lemon Drop
4 drops Sweetleaf Stevia Valencia Orange
1 tsp. fresh mint, finely chopped
1 tsp. fresh parsley, finely chopped
1 tsp. fresh basil, finely chopped

1. Preheat the oven to 375° F.
2. Slice the fennel bulb into ¼-inch pieces, cutting downward from the top. Cut out the tough stem area, but keep the slices intact.
3. Place the fennel in a single layer on a nonstick baking sheet with a rim. Pour ½ cup of the broth over the fennel, season with salt and pepper, and roast in the oven, turning occasionally, until the fennel is crisp tender and slightly golden around the edges, 25 to 30 minutes. Add a bit more broth if needed to prevent sticking.
4. Meanwhile, in a small bowl, combine the lemon and orange juice, Stevia, and chopped herbs. When the fennel is cooked, transfer with a spatula to a serving dish, and cover with the prepared citrus herb dressing. Serve immediately.

Makes 1 serving (100 calories; 1 vegetable, ½ fruit, ½ lemon)

Super Sautéed Onions

Just the ticket to top a grilled steak, these super delicious onions have a hint of sweetness with a bold oregano finish.

½ cup Basic Beef Broth (see page 21)
8 drops Sweetleaf Stevia Grape
1 tsp. red wine vinegar

1 cup onions, sliced
Salt and pepper to taste
Dash garlic powder
1 tsp. fresh oregano, finely chopped

1. Heat the broth in a nonstick skillet. Stir in the Stevia and vinegar and bring to a low simmer.
2. Add the onions, season with salt, pepper, and garlic powder, and cook over medium heat, stirring often, until soft and tender, about 10 minutes. Stir in the oregano and cook another minute. Serve immediately.

Makes 1 serving (80 calories; 1 vegetable)

Curried Spinach Sauté

Ideal as a side dish for any curry-flavored grilled chicken, spinach gets its exciting flair from fresh ginger and a hint of coconut.

½ cup Basic Chicken Broth (see page 21)
1 garlic clove, minced
1 tsp. fresh ginger, chopped
½ tsp. mild curry powder

4 drops Capella Coconut
3 cups leaf spinach, tough stems removed
Salt and pepper to taste

1. Heat the broth in a large nonstick skillet. Add the garlic, ginger, curry, and Capella and allow to simmer on low for 2 minutes.
2. Add the spinach, season with salt and pepper, increase the heat to medium, and cook, uncovered, stirring often, until the spinach has wilted, about 3 minutes. Serve immediately.

Makes 1 serving (40 calories; 1 vegetable)

Buttery Creamed Spinach

This is a great and flavorful side dish for any type of protein selection, especially grilled fish or seafood.

3 cups raw spinach
½ cup any Basic Broth (see pages 21 and 22)
Salt and pepper to taste

8 drops Capella Butter
1 Tbsp. milk
Dash paprika

1. Place the spinach leaves and broth in a large nonstick skillet and bring to a simmer over medium-high heat. When the spinach has reduced a little, add the salt and pepper and Capella drops. Continue to cook until the spinach is completely wilted and the liquid has evaporated.
2. Transfer the mixture to a food processor, add the milk and paprika, and pulse until creamed. Serve immediately.

Makes 1 serving (45 calories; 1 vegetable, 1 milk)

Italian Herbed Stewed Tomatoes

Delicious as a side for beef, chicken, or fish, this classic vegetable dish is livened up with the fresh flavor of herbs and garlic.

2 medium tomatoes, cored and diced
¼ cup Basic Chicken Broth (see page 21)
6 drops Sweetleaf Stevia Grape
3 drops Sweetleaf Stevia Lemon Drop
2 garlic cloves, minced
¼ tsp. minced onion flakes

Salt and pepper to taste
Pinch dried oregano
1 tsp. fresh parsley, finely chopped
1 tsp. fresh basil, finely chopped
1 tsp. fresh marjoram, finely chopped

1. Place the tomatoes in a medium saucepan. In a small bowl, combine the broth and Stevia and pour over the tomatoes. Add the garlic, onion flakes, salt, pepper, and oregano. Bring to a simmer, and allow to cook, stirring often, until the tomatoes begin to break down but still hold their shape, 10 to 12 minutes.
2. Add the chopped fresh herbs, stir well to combine, and cook 2 more minutes on low. Serve immediately.

Makes 2 servings (40 calories; 1 vegetable)

Vegetarian Dishes

Tomato Bruschetta Omelet

The fresh flavors of tomato, garlic, and basil highlight this wonderful omelet recipe that's sure to satisfy. Try filling with garlic sautéed spinach or chard on other occasions.

For the Tomato Bruschetta:

1 medium tomato, cored, seeded, and diced
1 garlic clove, minced
Salt and pepper to taste

2 tsp. red wine vinegar
6 drops Sweetleaf Stevia Grape
Pinch dried oregano
2 tsp. fresh basil, chopped

For the Omelet:

1 whole egg plus 3 egg whites

1. In a small bowl, combine all the bruschetta ingredients and stir well. Set aside.
2. In a medium bowl, whisk together the egg and egg whites and a pinch of salt and pepper. Heat a nonstick skillet over medium heat. Pour the egg mixture into the skillet and turn the heat to low.
3. Cook the egg evenly by lifting the firm edges to allow the wet egg mixture to reach the bottom of the pan. Cover and continue to cook over the very lowest of heat until the top surface has set.
4. Spoon the bruschetta mixture onto one side of the omelet and carefully flip the other side over with a spatula. Cover and cook another minute. Slide onto a plate and serve immediately.

Makes 1 serving (165 calories; 1 protein, 1 vegetable)

Easy Onion Frittata

This frittata requires no flipping, making it simple and quick to prepare. A hint of orange brings out the best in the sweet onion sauté.

1 cup onions, sliced
Salt and pepper to taste
¼ tsp. dried thyme
Juice of ½ an orange

6 drops Sweetleaf Stevia Valencia Orange
1 whole egg plus 3 egg whites
½ orange, unpeeled, cut into circles

1. Heat a nonstick skillet over medium-high heat. Add the onions, salt, pepper, and thyme, and cook, stirring often, until the onions have softened, about 6 minutes. Add a little water, if necessary, to prevent sticking.
2. In a small bowl, combine the orange juice and Stevia. Pour over the onion mixture and cook 1 minute. In a medium bowl, whisk together the egg and egg whites with a pinch of salt and pepper. Pour into the skillet and move the onions evenly around.
3. Reduce the heat to low, cover, and cook until the bottom is lightly browned and the top is nearly set, 5 to 8 minutes. Remove the lid and place the skillet under a low broiler for a brief few seconds to finish cooking the top.
4. Loosen the sides of the frittata with a spatula and slide onto a plate. Serve immediately with the orange slices as garnish.

Makes 1 serving (275 calories; 1 protein, 1 vegetable, 1 fruit)

Sweet Strawberry Soufflé Omelet

You'll feel as if you're eating dessert for dinner with this wonderfully satisfying omelet that gets a boost of flavor and sweetness from Capella and Stevia.

10 strawberries, stemmed and diced
1 Tbsp. water
4 drops Capella Strawberries &
    Cream

10 drops Clear Stevia
1 whole egg
3 egg whites
Pinch of salt

1. In a medium bowl, stir together the strawberries, water, Capella, and Stevia. Set aside for 15 minutes.
2. In a large bowl, whisk the whole egg until pale yellow. In another large bowl, beat the egg whites with the salt, using an electric beater, to soft peaks. Fold the beaten egg whites in batches, into the beaten egg until well combined but still large in volume.
3. Heat a nonstick skillet over medium heat. Pour the egg mixture into the skillet, spread out evenly, reduce the heat to low, cover, and cook until set, 4 to 6 minutes.
4. Spoon the strawberry mixture over the omelet and fold over. Slide out of the skillet onto a plate and serve immediately.

Makes 1 serving (170 calories; 1 protein, 1 fruit)

Super Summer Salad with Creamy Dressing

Cottage cheese provides the protein and consistency in this terrific light main course salad for vegetarian eaters, enhanced with sweetly marinated orange supremes.

2 cups iceberg lettuce chunks

For the Supremes:

1 medium orange	6 drops Sweetleaf Stevia Valencia Orange
1 Tbsp. lemon juice	3 drops Sweetleaf Stevia Lemon Drop

For the Dressing:

½ cup nonfat cottage cheese	Juice of ½ a lemon
1 small garlic clove, minced	Juice from orange supremes (see instructions)
¼ tsp. dry mustard	
½ tsp. fresh parsley	3 drops Sweetleaf Stevia Valencia Orange
½ tsp. fresh chives	Salt and pepper to taste

1. To prepare the supremes, cut the ends off the orange and place flat on a cutting board. Using a sharp knife, remove all the rind and white pith from the outside. Cut in between the membranes of the orange to release the supremes and transfer to a small bowl. Squeeze the remaining membranes to release all juice into another small bowl and set aside. Combine the lemon juice and Stevia drops and stir into the bowl with the supremes. Transfer to the refrigerator to chill.
2. Meanwhile, make the dressing by adding all the ingredients to the bowl with the orange juice. Transfer to a blender and puree until smooth. Taste for seasoning and chill.
3. When ready to serve, place the lettuce chunks on a plate and top with the dressing. Place the supremes decoratively around and add a grinding of black pepper to finish. Serve immediately.

Makes 1 serving (170 calories; 1 protein, 1 vegetable, 1 fruit, ½ lemon)

Apple Delight Cottage Cheese Dip

For those who prefer to "dip" into their protein, this wonderful treat is perfect for a light lunch or supper, flavored with sweetly spiced apple with the help of Capella and Stevia.

For the Dip:

½ apple, peeled and grated
1 tsp. lemon juice
6 drops Capella Green Apple

10 drops Clear Stevia
½ cup nonfat cottage cheese
Dash ground cinnamon

To Dip:

½ apple, cored and sliced
Celery sticks (about 2 cups)

Melba toast

1. In a small bowl, combine the grated apple, lemon juice, Capella, and Stevia. Set aside for 10 minutes.
2. Stir the cottage cheese into the apple mixture and transfer to a small dipping bowl. Top with a dash of cinnamon and refrigerate until ready to serve.
3. Meanwhile prepare a plate with the sliced apple, celery sticks, and Melba. Place the bowl with the dip in the middle and serve immediately.

Makes 1 serving (215 calories; 1 protein, 1 vegetable, 1 fruit)

So-y Delicious Chili

Plain soy patties take on the zesty flavors of Mexico in this easy chili dish that's both satisfying and delicious.

2 medium tomatoes, cored, seeded, and diced
1 garlic clove, minced
½ tsp. onion flakes
1 Tbsp. chili powder
1 tsp. paprika
¼ tsp. ground cumin

Salt and pepper to taste
1 cup Basic Vegetable Broth (see page 22)
6 drops Sweetleaf Stevia Grape
2 soy patties, cooked and crumbled (ground beef or buffalo can be substituted)

1. In a medium saucepan, combine the tomatoes, garlic, and onion flakes and bring to a simmer. Cook over low heat, stirring often, until the tomatoes begin to break down, about 4 minutes. Add the chili powder, paprika, cumin, salt, and pepper and cook 1 minute.
2. Combine the broth and Stevia and pour into the tomato mixture. Bring to a simmer and stir in the soy patties. Cook over low heat, stirring occasionally, until thickened, about 20 minutes. Taste for seasoning and serve immediately.

Makes 2 servings (145 calories; 1 protein, 1 vegetable)

Mighty Good Meat-Free Meatloaf

This delicious look-a-like is easy to prepare, topped with a terrific sweet ketchup glaze.

For the Loaf:

4 soy patties, defrosted (if necessary) and crumbled
Salt and pepper to taste
1 tsp. dried parsley
½ tsp. onion flakes
½ tsp. garlic powder

2 Tbsp. milk
2 Tbsp. Bragg Liquid Aminos
1 Tbsp. lemon juice
5 drops Sweetleaf Stevia Lemon Drop
2 breadsticks or Melba toast, crushed into crumbs

For the Glaze:

1 Tbsp. Oven-Roasted Tomato Ketchup (see page 47)

1 Tbsp. Basic Vegetable Broth (see page 22)
6 drops Sweetleaf Stevia Grape

1. Preheat the oven to 350° F.
2. In a large mixing bowl, combine all the loaf ingredients and mix well with your hands. Shape into a long oval and place in a nonstick loaf pan.
3. In a small bowl, combine the glaze ingredients and spread on top of the loaf. Cover with foil and bake for 30 minutes.
4. Remove the foil, baste with any accumulated juices, and continue to cook until the internal temperature reaches 165° F and the loaf is nicely browned and glazed, about 20 minutes more. Let rest for 10 minutes before slicing and serving.

Makes 4 servings (160 calories; 1 protein, 1 vegetable, ½ breadstick, ½ milk)

Soy Meatballs with Asian Ginger Orange Sauce

These delectable morsels will satisfy any craving for a hearty "meat" dish, thanks to the flavors of Asia and a touch of zesty sweetness from Stevia.

For the Meatballs:

4 soy patties, defrosted and crumbled
2 tsp. fresh ginger, minced

1 garlic clove, minced
Salt and pepper to taste

For the Sauce:

Juice of 2 oranges
½ cup Basic Vegetable Broth (see page 22)
10 drops Sweetleaf Stevia Valencia Orange
6 drops Capella Orange Creamsicle

¼ cup Bragg Liquid Aminos
2-inch piece fresh ginger, peeled and thinly sliced
½ tsp. orange zest
Salt and pepper to taste

1. In a medium bowl, combine all the meatball ingredients and form into balls the size of walnuts.
2. Heat a nonstick skillet over medium-high heat and fry the meatballs until lightly browned, 8 to 10 minutes. Remove and set aside.
3. Combine the sauce ingredients in the skillet and bring to a simmer. Allow to cook for 1 minute, return the meatballs to the pan, and cook over low heat, stirring occasionally, until the sauce has thickened and the meatballs are cooked through, about 10 minutes. Serve immediately.

Makes 4 servings (160 calories; 1 protein, ½ fruit)

Italian-Style Soy Meatballs

Marinara sauce enfolds these delicious meatballs that are full of sunny Italian flavor and great for a hearty and satisfying supper.

For the Meatballs:

2 soy patties, defrosted (if necessary) and crumbled

1 garlic clove, minced

2 tsp. red wine vinegar or apple cider vinegar

4 drops Sweetleaf Stevia Grape

1 breadstick, crushed into crumbs

¼ tsp. dried oregano

¼ tsp. dried basil

¼ tsp. dried parsley

Salt and pepper to taste

One recipe of Nonna's Marinara Sauce (see page 77) made with Basic Vegetable Broth.

1. In a medium bowl, combine all the meatball ingredients and shape into bite-sized balls.
2. Heat a nonstick skillet over medium-high heat and fry the meatballs until lightly browned. Add the marinara sauce, stir to coat, cover, and cook over low heat until the meatballs are cooked through, about 10 minutes. Stir occasionally to prevent sticking. Serve immediately.

Makes 2 servings (150 calories; 1 protein, 1 vegetable, ½ breadstick)

Spinach Soy Patties with Lemon Sauce Glaze

Doctored-up soy patties get a boost of flavor from garlic sautéed spinach and a tangy lemon glaze.

3 cups baby spinach
1 garlic clove, minced
Salt and pepper to taste
2 soy patties, defrosted (if necessary) and crumbled
¼ tsp. lemon zest

½ cup Basic Vegetable Broth (see page 22)
Juice of ½ a lemon
8 drops Sweetleaf Stevia Lemon Drop
½ lemon with rind, sliced thin

1. In a large nonstick skillet over medium heat, sauté the spinach with the garlic, salt and pepper until just wilted. Set aside to cool.
2. Chop the spinach mixture and combine in a medium bowl with the soy patties and lemon zest. Form into 4 patties and refrigerate for 20 minutes.
3. Heat a nonstick skillet over medium-high heat and fry the patties, browning on both sides, about 5 minutes in all. Combine the broth, lemon juice, and Stevia in a small bowl and add to the skillet, swirling to coat the patties. Place the lemon slices on top of the patties, cover, reduce the heat to low, and cook an additional 2 minutes. Serve immediately.

Makes 2 servings (130 calories; 1 protein, ½ vegetable, ¼ lemon)

SNACKS AND DESSERTS

FROM WARM AND WONDERFUL TREATS to frozen fruity delights, desserts and tasty sweet snacks are not forgotten thanks to the great flavors of Capella and Stevia. Transforming simple ingredients into delicious gourmet-tasting selections has never been easier!

When recipes call for cottage cheese or egg whites, be sure to count these toward your protein serving, and be mindful of the breadstick and milk allowances. All these are clearly marked at the end of each recipe to help you keep track.

Italian Hazelnut Café Granita
(Recipe on page 130)

Warm Desserts and Baked Snacks

Cinnamon Baked Apple

This baked apple version will become a real favorite with the delightful flavor of cream soda and cinnamon.

1 firm apple, such as Gala or Golden Delicious

Dash ground cinnamon

½ cup Super Vanilla Cream Soda (see page 3)

1 Tbsp. crushed Apple Crisp snacks

1. Preheat oven to 375° F.
2. Stem and core apple using a melon baller or grapefruit knife and place in a small baking dish.
3. Sprinkle the cinnamon on top and pour the soda inside and around the apple.
4. Bake until fork tender but still firm, about 40 minutes.
5. Just before serving, sprinkle with the crushed Apple Crisp snacks.

Makes 1 serving (95 calories; 1 fruit)

Warm Caramel Apple with Vanilla Sauce

Apples and caramel always make for a winning team and here, a touch of delicious vanilla sauce really takes this treat over the top.

1 firm apple, such as Gala or Golden Delicious

¼ cup purified water

5 drops Capella Caramel

4 drops Clear Stevia, or more to taste

Dash ground cinnamon

Dash ground nutmeg

1 Tbsp. milk

5 drops Sweetleaf Stevia Vanilla Crème

1. Stem, core, and dice the apple into ½-inch cubes and place in a small saucepan.
2. Combine the water, Capella, and Clear Stevia in a measuring cup and pour over the apples. Stir in the cinnamon and nutmeg.
3. Cook over medium heat, stirring often, until apples are softened, but still firm. Meanwhile, combine the milk with the Stevia Vanilla drops.
4. Remove apples from heat, cool slightly, then transfer to a dish and serve warm with the vanilla sauce spooned over.

Makes 1 serving (100 calories; 1 fruit, 1 milk)

Apple Gingerbread Crumble

The enticing spices of sweet gingerbread highlight this dessert that's particularly tasty straight from the oven.

For the Apple:
1 apple, cored and thinly sliced
1 tsp. lemon juice
4 drops Clear Stevia

For the Topping:
1 Melba toast, finely crumbled
6 to 8 drops Capella Gingerbread
¼ tsp. powdered Stevia

1. Preheat the oven to 375° F.
2. Overlap the apple slices in the bottom of a medium-sized ramekin or oven-proof dish and sprinkle with the lemon juice and Clear Stevia.
3. In a small bowl, combine the crumbs, Capella, and powdered Stevia and sprinkle on top of the apples. Bake until the apples are fork tender and the topping is slightly crisped, about 15 minutes.

Makes 1 serving (115 calories; 1 fruit, 1 Melba)

Baked Apple with Pralines and Cream

Warm and wonderful, with the sweet aroma of praline "burnt" sugar, you'll love this treat even more every time you make it.

For the Apple:
1 firm apple, such as Gala or Golden Delicious
½ cup water
3 or 4 drops Capella Pralines & Cream
8 drops Clear Stevia

For the Topping:
1 Melba toast, crumbled
1 Tbsp. milk
2 or 3 drops Capella Pralines & Cream

1. Preheat oven to 375° F.
2. Stem and core apple using a melon baller or grapefruit knife and place in a small baking dish.
3. Combine the water, Capella, and Stevia and pour inside and around the apple.
4. Bake until fork tender but still firm, about 40 minutes.
5. Just before serving, combine the topping ingredients in a small saucepan (or heat in the microwave) and pour over the baked apple.

Makes 1 serving (125 calories; 1 fruit, 1 Melba, 1 milk)

Sweet Hot Toddy Apples

A dessert and a nightcap all in one, you'll love the amazing aroma and terrific taste.

2 medium apples, peeled, cored, and cut into chunks
1 Tbsp. lemon juice
3 Tbsp. water

3 to 5 drops Capella Butter
3 to 5 drops Capella Irish Cream
10 to 12 drops Clear Stevia

1. Place the apple chunks in a medium saucepan. Stir together the remaining ingredients in a small bowl and pour over the apples.
2. Cook covered, stirring occasionally, over medium-low heat, until the apples are somewhat softened, about 4 minutes. Serve warm or chilled.

Makes 2 servings (95 calories; 1 fruit)

Grilled Cinnamon Apple Slices

1 apple, such as Gala, cut into ¼-inch slices from top to bottom
2 Tbsp. water

6 drops Capella Apple Pie
1 tsp. lemon juice
10 drops Clear Stevia
Ground cinnamon for sprinkling

1. Place the apple slices in a single layer in a shallow dish. Combine the water, Capella, lemon juice, and Stevia and drizzle over the apples. Turn and toss to coat. Set aside.
2. Just before grilling, sprinkle the apples with cinnamon. Place on the grill over medium heat and grill until nicely marked and heated through, about 3 minutes per side.
3. Transfer to a clean dish and serve.

Makes 1 serving. (100 calories; 1 fruit)

Orange Chocolate Compote

The flavors of orange and chocolate combine beautifully here in this terrific treat that's perfect for dessert or as a sweet in-between-meal snack.

1 orange, peeled and cut into
   supremes, juice reserved

2 Tbsp. water
12 drops Sweetleaf Stevia Chocolate

1. To prepare the supremes, cut the ends off the orange and place flat on a cutting board. Using a sharp knife, remove all the rind and white pith from the outside. Cut in between the membranes of the orange to release the supremes and transfer to a small bowl.
2. Place all the ingredients in a small saucepan including any reserved orange juice. Bring to a simmer over medium heat and allow to cook, stirring often, until heated through and fragrant, about 3 minutes. Taste and add more Stevia, if desired. Serve warm or chilled.

Makes 1 serving (70 calories; 1 fruit)

Strawberry Crumble with Sabayon

You'll love this gourmet treat that's bursting with sweet strawberries and classic Italian flair.

10 strawberries, stemmed and sliced
2 Tbsp. plus 2 tsp. purified water
10 drops Sweetleaf Stevia Berry
9 drops Clear Stevia

1 breadstick, crushed
1 Tbsp. milk
3 drops Capella Italian Egg Nog

1. Preheat oven to 350° F.
2. Place the strawberries in a shallow, single-serve baking dish. Combine 2 tablespoons of the water in a measuring cup with the Stevia Berry and pour over the strawberries.
3. In a small bowl, stir together the remaining 2 tsp. of water with 5 drops of Clear Stevia. Using a fork, stir in the breadstick crumbs.
4. Sprinkle the moistened crumbs over the strawberries and bake until bubbly and toasted on top, 20 to 25 minutes. Meanwhile, warm the milk with the Capella Italian Egg Nog and the remaining 4 drops of Clear Stevia and spoon over just before serving.

Makes 1 serving (55 calories; 1 fruit, 1 breadstick, 1 milk)

Simple Strawberry Surprise

This easy way of sweetening up your strawberry selection is perfect with the occasional cottage cheese protein and always great even on its own.

10 strawberries, stemmed and sliced
10 drops Sweetleaf Stevia Berry
2 Tbsp. purified water
1 tsp. lemon juice

½ cup nonfat cottage cheese
1 Tbsp. Brothers Strawberry Crisp snacks, crushed

1. Place the strawberries in a small bowl. Stir together the Stevia Berry, water, and lemon juice in a measuring cup and pour over the strawberries, stirring gently to coat. Refrigerate, stirring occasionally, for at least 30 minutes.
2. Spoon the cottage cheese into a serving dish. Top with the flavored sliced strawberries, sprinkle with the crushed Strawberry Crisp snacks, and serve.

Makes 1 serving (80 calories; 1 fruit, ½ protein)

Strawberry Fudge Brownie

Two great flavors come together thanks to Capella and Stevia in this tasty treat that's almost as good as the real thing.

5 strawberries, stemmed and roughly chopped
2 Melba toast, finely crumbled

8 drops Capella Chocolate Fudge Brownie
¼ tsp. powdered Stevia, or more to taste

1. In a small bowl, stir together all the ingredients and taste for flavor and sweetness.
2. Press the mixture into a small dish and cover with plastic wrap. Allow to chill in the refrigerator for at least 2 hours. Cut into pieces and serve.

Makes 2 servings (35 calories; ¼ fruit, 1 Melba)

Mini Strawberry Cheesecakes

Unbelievable but true: cheesecake with a tempting graham cracker "crust" is on the menu. Enjoy well chilled and savor each bite!

For the Crust:

2 Melba toasts, crumbled	8 drops Capella Graham Cracker
1 Tbsp. purified water	8 drops Clear Stevia

For the Cheesecake:

½ cup nonfat cottage cheese	5 strawberries, stemmed and sliced
8 drops Sweetleaf Stevia Berry	

1. Preheat the oven to 350° F. In a small bowl, combine the crumbled Melba, water, and Capella and Clear Stevia with a fork.
2. Divide the crumb mixture between two small ramekins and firmly press down and around to form a crust. Place on a cookie sheet and bake until the crumbs are just firm and lightly browned, 12 to 15 minutes. Set aside to cool.
3. Meanwhile, whisk together, or use a blender, to combine the cottage cheese and Stevia Berry to a smooth consistency. Divide and pour into the two cooled ramekins and place the strawberry slices decoratively on top. Chill at least 2 hours, preferably overnight, before serving.

Makes 2 servings (65 calories; ¼ fruit, ½ protein, 1 Melba)

Caramelized Grapefruit

Enjoy this sweet treat any time of day when a craving for fruity sweetness arrives. Try substituting other Capella and Stevia flavors for unlimited variety.

½ medium grapefruit, seeded	½ breadstick, finely crumbled
6 to 8 drops Sweetleaf Stevia English Toffee	⅛ tsp. powdered Stevia

1. Preheat the broiler to high. Cover a shallow baking pan with foil.
2. Cut a small sliver from the bottom of the grapefruit half so it will sit without wobbling. Using a grapefruit or sharp paring knife, cut between the fruit membrane to loosen the segments. Drip the Stevia into the cut between the rind and the fruit.
3. Combine the breadstick crumbs and powdered Stevia and sprinkle on top. Broil until the grapefruit top is lightly browned and warmed, turning the pan to heat evenly. Serve immediately.

Makes 1 serving (62 calories; 1 fruit, ½ breadstick)

Pumpkin Cheesecake Bites

A true holiday favorite, these cheesecake delights, complete with graham cracker crust, will help you savor the festivities.

For the Crust:

2 Melba toasts, crumbled   8 drops Capella Graham Cracker
1 Tbsp. purified water   8 drops Clear Stevia

For the Filling:

½ cup nonfat cottage cheese   8 to 10 drops Clear Stevia
4 or 5 drops Capella Pumpkin Pie
   Spice

1. Preheat the oven to 350° F. In a small bowl, combine the crumbled Melba, water, Capella, and Clear Stevia with a fork to make the crust.
2. Divide the crumb mixture between two small ramekins and firmly press down and around to form a crust. Place on a cookie sheet and bake until the crumbs are just firm and lightly browned, 12 to 15 minutes. Set aside to cool.
3. Meanwhile, whisk together, or use a blender, to combine the cottage cheese with the Capella Pumpkin Pie Spice and Clear Stevia. Divide and pour into the two cooled ramekins and chill at least 2 hours before serving.

Makes 2 servings (65 calories; ½ protein, 1 Melba)

Refreshing Frozen Treats

Apple Pie Sorbet

This delicious and refreshing dessert gets a wonderful hint of apple pie flavor from Capella and is easy as pie to make!

2 medium apples, peeled, cored, and diced
1 Tbsp. lemon juice

6 to 8 drops Capella Apple Pie
10 to 12 drops Clear Stevia

1. Combine all the ingredients in a small saucepan and cook over medium-low heat, stirring often, until the apples are soft. Set aside to cool.
2. Taste for the addition of flavor and Clear Stevia, and puree in a blender until smooth. Transfer to two ramekins or small dishes, cover the surfaces with plastic wrap, and freeze until solid but still somewhat soft, about 2 hours. Serve immediately.

Makes 2 servings (100 calories; 1 fruit)

Tropical Grapefruit Granita

Tangy grapefruit juice combines with delicious pineapple and coconut for a super refreshing and delightful dessert or snack perfect for a hot day.

Juice of 1 grapefruit
2 tsp. lemon juice

8 to 10 drops Capella with Stevia Piña Colada
1 Tbsp. water

1. Stir together all the ingredients and taste for additional sweetness or flavor. Pour into a shallow, freezer-proof container and freeze uncovered.
2. Every 15 to 20 minutes, use the tines of a fork to fluff the ice mixture and return to the freezer. When the mixture appears sno-cone like, it is ready to serve.

Makes 2 servings (0 calories)

Old Time Orange Creamsicle

Who doesn't love the sensational combination of orange and vanilla in a creamy and cool dessert? Use popsicle molds or mini paper cups with sticks to shape, or simply freeze in the orange rind shell.

Juice of 2 oranges
2 Tbsp. milk

10 to 12 drops Capella Orange Creamsicle
15 drops Clear Stevia

Combine all the ingredients in a blender and pour into molds. Freeze for several hours or overnight before serving.

Makes 2 servings (80 calories; 1 fruit, 1 milk)

Frozen Strawberries and Cream

Delightfully sweet and wonderfully refreshing, make this early in the day for a great after dinner treat.

10 strawberries, stemmed and roughly chopped
¼ tsp. powdered Clear Stevia
1 Tbsp. milk

8 drops Capella Strawberries & Cream
2 Tbsp. water

1. Place the chopped berries in a bowl, sprinkle with the Stevia, and set aside for 30 minutes, stirring occasionally.
2. Using a slotted spoon, remove about ⅓ of the strawberries from the bowl and place in a freezable bowl or container.
3. Combine the rest of the strawberries and any accumulated liquid with the remaining ingredients and puree in a food processor until smooth. Pour into the dish with the reserved strawberries, stir, and cover with plastic wrap. Freeze for several hours until solid but still somewhat soft before serving.

Makes 1 serving (40 calories; 1 fruit, 1 milk)

Frozen Chocolate-Dipped Strawberries

This take on a favorite treat is both refreshing and delicious as a snack or dessert, but keep track of how many you pop in your mouth!

10 strawberries with stems

5 to 6 drops Sweetleaf Stevia Chocolate

1. Line a baking sheet with parchment or waxed paper.
2. Poke each of the strawberries with a toothpick about 10 times in different places. Put the berries on the prepared pan an inch apart and drizzle about 5 or 6 of the chocolate drops over each.
3. Place the pan in the freezer and freeze the berries until just solid on the outside, about 1½ hours. Serve immediately.

Makes 1 serving (30 calories; 1 fruit)

Italian Hazelnut Café Granita

Granita ice desserts are easy to make even without ice cream makers or blenders. Try this delicious coffee- and hazelnut-flavored version or substitute other Capella or Stevia flavors for variety.

2 cups cold brewed coffee
10 to 12 Sweetleaf Stevia Hazelnut

4 to 6 drops Capella Cappuccino
8 to 10 Clear Stevia drops

1. Stir together all the ingredients and taste for additional sweetness or flavor. Pour into a shallow, freezer-proof container and freeze uncovered.
2. Every 15 to 20 minutes, use the tines of a fork to fluff the ice mixture and return to the freezer. When the mixture appears sno-cone like, it is ready to serve.

Makes 2 servings (0 calories)

Italian Ice Medley

Make this delicious array of refreshing old-fashioned Italian ices to have on hand when a craving for something icy and sweet arrives. Experiment with as many Capella and Stevia flavors as you like. If using food coloring, be sure the product is protocol safe.

For the Base Ice Medley:
3 cups purified water
Juice of ½ a lemon
6 ½-cup-sized sturdy paper cups

For Blueberry Raspberry:
3 drops Capella Blueberry
4 drops Capella Raspberry
12 to 15 Clear Stevia
Blue and red food coloring (optional)

For Classic Lemon:
15 drops Sweetleaf Stevia
    Lemon Drop
Yellow food coloring (optional)

For Root Beer Float:
12 drops Sweetleaf Stevia
    Root Beer
4 drops Sweetleaf Stevia
    Vanilla Crème
Light brown food coloring
    (optional)

1. Combine the water with the lemon juice and divide into 3 bowls. Add the appropriate drops for the flavored ices (and coloring if using) to the bowls and taste each for sweetness and flavor.
2. Pour into the paper cups (making 2 of each flavor) and freeze until just solid. Allow the ices, if desired, to sit out for 10 minutes to soften before serving.

Makes 6 servings (1 calorie)

HCG PROTOCOL
Maintenance Phase

THE **MAINTENANCE PHASE** lasts six weeks and is a critical part of the HCG Protocol. You will eat to stabilize your new metabolic rate and create a new set-point weight, thus preventing your body from naturally gaining back to its previous set-point. This is why the HCG Protocol is known as the only long-term weight-loss solution!

The two parts of Maintenance are M1 and M2, three weeks each. During M1, you must eat enough calories, get plenty of protein, go easy on the "Caution" foods, and avoid anything not listed in the Maintenance Food Guide. During M2, you will slowly add starches and sugars over the three weeks while keeping your weight within two pounds from what it was on the last day you took HCG.

For many people, getting enough calories in M1 can be frustrating even though the food choices are greatly expanded. To get the necessary number of calories in protein, vegetables, and fruits to support your new BMR (basal metabolic rate), you need to get creative!

With the help of these mouth-watering recipes, you'll breeze right through Maintenance, and permanent weight loss will be yours. Some of these dishes will likely remain favorites long after you've reached your goal!

ThinNow Maintenance 1 (M1) Guide

M1 "No Caution" Foods

Here is a list of foods you can eat during M1 without endangering the resetting of your metabolism or the stabilization of your new weight. This is the "go-to" list for your meals and snacks in M1.

You must calculate your BMR to get the right number of daily calories. The more you weigh and the more active you are, the more calories you need. The leading cause of weight gain in maintenance is not eating enough!

Here is the schedule we suggest you use to stabilize your weight as quickly as possible:

M1 Week 1: Eat 0 "Caution" foods.

M1 Week 2: Eat 1 to 2 "Caution" foods per day, only if you did not have to do a steak day in Week 1. Otherwise, continue with the Week 1 suggestion until your weight is stable.

M1 Week 3: Eat 2 to 3 "Caution" foods per day if your weight was stable in Week 2. Your goal is to gradually add "Caution" foods and stabilize while doing so, as that will make Maintenance 2 and beyond very easy!

ITEM	Cals/Oz.	ITEM	Cals/Oz.
Beverages			
Coffee (all types, no sugar)	0	Tomato Juice	5
Espresso	0	Vegetable Juice (V8)	6
Tea (all types, no sugar)	0	Water (all varieties of 0-calorie)	0
Lemon or Lime Juice (fresh)	7	Perrier, Club Soda	0
Almond Milk (unsweetened only)	*	Soy Milk (unsweetened only)	*
Fish (Average serving = 4 oz.) Farmed have different caloric value.			
Bass (Sea and Striped)	27	Salmon	
Burbot	25	Atlantic (wild)	40
Butterfish	41	Chinook	50
Carp	36	Chum	34
Catfish (farmed)	33	Coho (wild)	41
Cod (Atlantic & Pacific)	23/19	Pink	36
Croaker	29	Sockeye	40
Cusk	24	Shark	36
Devilfish (Alaskan)	27	Snapper	28
Drum Fish	33	Sole	20
Flounder	20	Sturgeon	29

* = check product label for calories

ITEM	Cals/Oz.	ITEM	Cals/Oz.
Grouper	26	Swordfish	40
Haddock	21	Tilapia	27
Halibut (Atlantic & Pacific)	35	Tilefish	27
Halibut (Greenland)	52	Trout	
Herring (Atlantic)	42	Brown	41
Ling, Ling Cod	24	Rainbow (wild)	33
Mahi-Mahi	24	Sea	29
Monkfish	21	Tuna	
Mullet (Striped)	33	Bluefin	40
Northern Pike	25	Skipjack	29
Orange Perch (Atlantic)	22	Yellowfin	31
Orange Roughy	21	Turbot	27
Pike (Walleye)	26	Whitefish	38
Pollock (Atlantic)	26	Whiting	25
Rockfish (Pacific)	25	Wolffish	27
Sablefish	55		
Shellfish (Calories listed are per ounce. Average serving = 4 oz.)			
Crab		Lobster	22
Blue, Dungeness, King	24–25	Oysters	14–23
Queen	25	Scallops	19
Crayfish (wild)	22	Shrimp	20
Meat (Calories listed are per ounce. Average serving = 4 oz.)			
Beef		Lamb – Ground	79
Bottom Round	35–54	Loin	37–87
Brisket	34–78	Ribs	45–81
Chuck Roast	32–78	Ostrich – Ground	46
Eye Round	33–49	Top Loin	33
Filet Mignon or Tenderloin	41–77	Pheasant	37
Flank Steak	38–46	Pork – Chop or Roast	34–80
Lean Ground	38–93	Chop Sirloin	35–40
Ribeye	41–76	Ground	33–74
Short Ribs	48–108	Ribs	62–78
Top Sirloin	35–60	Rinds (½ oz.)	76
T-bone	53–65	Tenderloin	30–34
Top Roast	39–49	Quail	38
Bison – Ground	41–62	Veal – Breast	58
Roast	31–55	Ground	40

The Ultimate HCG Diet Cookbook

ITEM	Cals/Oz.	ITEM	Cals/Oz.
Chicken (no skin)		Leg	29–32
Dark	35	Loin	32–45
White	32	Rib	33–45
Duck – Breast	34	Shank Roast	30–32
Whole (domestic)	113	Shoulder	31–36
Emu (ground)	38	Sirloin	30–42
Goose (with skin)	104	Turkey (white & dark, no skin)	31
Goat	31	Venison	34
Eggs & Protein Shakes			
Egg (1 large/1 extra-large)	71/80	Tempeh (1 oz.)	54*
Protein Powder (0-5 carbs, sweetened with Stevia)	100-120*	TVP (Textured Vegetable Protein, ¼ cup dry)	80
Seitan (1 oz.)	30*	Tofu (firm, 1 oz.)	35*
Fruit (Calories listed are per ounce. Average serving = 1/2 cup)			
Apple	15	Kiwi	17
Applesauce (unsweetened)	*	Lemon	7
Apricot	13	Lime	7
Avocado	45	Loganberries	15
Blackberries	12	Mulberries	12
Blueberries	16	Nectarine	12
Cherries – Red Sour	14	Orange	13
Sweet	18	Papaya	11
Coconut (dried, unsweetened)	185	Peach	11
Cranberries (fresh)	13	Pear	16
Currants	16	Pineapple	14
Elderberries	20	Plum	13
Figs (raw)	21	Raspberries	15
Grapefruit – Pink & Red	9	Rhubarb	6
White	9	Strawberries	10
Gooseberries	12	Tangerine (Mandarin Orange)	15
Vegetables (Calories listed are per ounce. Average serving = 1/2 cup)			
Alfalfa Sprouts	6	Mung Bean Sprouts	8
Artichoke	13	Mustard Greens	7
Asparagus	6	Mushrooms	
Bamboo Shoots	8	Brown, Cremini, Italian	6
Beet Greens	6	Enoki	10
Broccoli	10	Morel, Porcini, Portobello	6
Brussels Sprouts	12	Onions	11

* = check product label for calories

ITEM	Cals/Oz.	ITEM	Cals/Oz.
Cabbage (red or white)	7	Peas (Snow)	12
Carrots	11	Peppers – Banana	8
Cauliflower	7	Bell	6
Celery	4	Hot Green & Red	11
Collard Greens	8	Radish	4
Cucumber (peeled)	3	Seaweed (Kelp)	12
Eggplant	7	Snap Beans (green & yellow)	9
Endive	5	Spinach	6
Fennel	9	Squash – Scallop	5
Green Beans	9	Straight Neck, Summer	5
Kale	14	Zucchini	5
Lettuce		Swiss Chard	5
Bibb, Boston, Butter, Iceberg	4	Tomato (red, green, orange)	5, 6, 4
Romaine	5	Turnip	8
Nuts, Nut Butters, Seeds, Oils			
Coconut (1 oz. dried, unsweetened)	185	Olive Oil (1 Tbsp.)	124
Flax Seeds (1 oz.)	150	Coconut Oil (1 Tbsp.)	121
Condiments (Check labels; watch for added sugars)			
Capers (1 Tbsp.)	3	Vinegar (apple cider, balsamic, brown rice, champagne, distilled, garlic wine, golden balsamic, Italian herb, malt, red wine, rice, tarragon, white distilled, white wine)	3-25/ Tbsp. Check label
Horseradish (1 Tbsp.)	7		
Mustard (1 Tbsp., no sugars)	9-12		
Olives (1 oz., black, green)	32		
Pickles (1 oz. dill, not sweet)	3		
Salsa (2 Tbsp., check for sugar)	10-25*	Wasabi Sauce (1 Tbsp.)	15
Soy Sauce (1 Tbsp.)	8	Worcestershire Sauce (1 Tbsp.)	11
Spices/Seasonings/Sweeteners (Check labels; watch for added sugars)			
Allspice, Basil, Bay Leaf, Cayenne Pepper, Celery Salt, Chili Powder, Chili Seasoning, Chinese Style Five Spice, Cilantro (fresh), Cinnamon, Cocoa (unsweetened), Coriander, Creole Seasoning, Cumin (ground), Dill (fresh, seed), Garlic (cloves, granules, powder, salt), Ginger, McCormick (Broiled Steak Seasoning Salt, Garlic Pepper Grinder, Herb Chicken Seasonings, Italian Herb Seasoning Grinder, Rotisserie Chicken Seasoning, Steakhouse Seasoning Grinder)		Mint Leaves (dried, fresh), Nutmeg, Onion (powder, salt), Oregano (dried), Paprika, Parsley (fresh, dried), Pepper (ground, peppercorns), Poultry Seasoning, Reese All-Purpose Steak Salt, Rosemary (fresh, dried), Sage (dried), Salt, Spice Islands (Herbes De Provence, Ground Chipotle), Stevia (Sweetleaf and KAL brands are safe), Thyme, Thyme Leaves, Tony Chachere's Original Creole Seasoning, Tumeric, Weber Grill Creations N'Orleans Cajun Seasoning, White Pepper	
Sauces and Gravy* (Check labels; watch for added sugars)			
Au Jus Gravy, Creole Sauce, Curry Sauce, Marinara, Mole Verde, Mushroom, Oyster, Taco Sauce – Red or Green, Tamari			

* = check product label for sugar and calories

M1 "Caution" Foods

Here are the "Caution" foods for M1. The trick to eating them is not to have too many, but there is no set number for "too many." See page 135 for our suggested guide to adding "Caution" foods to stabilize your weight as quickly as possible.

ITEM	Cals/Oz.	ITEM	Cals/Oz.
Caution Meat (No sugar added is preferred)			
Bacon* (2 slices)	105	Hot Dogs* (1 serving)	120-200
Canadian Bacon* (1 serving)	60-90	Jerky* (2 oz. beef, pork, turkey, venison)	120-180
Deli/Lunch Meats (1 serving*)	80-200	Sausage* (1 serving)	120-250
Caution Nuts & Nut Butters (Limit to 1 ounce per serving)			
Almonds		Hazelnuts	176
Butter	177	Macadamia Nuts	201
Flour	160	Mixed Nuts	173
Nuts	190	Peanut Butter* (no sugar)	85-100
Paste	128	Peanuts	159
Brazil Nuts	190	Pecans	193
Coconut Flour (2 Tbsp.)	60	Walnuts	183
Caution Dairy Products (Limit to 1 ounce per serving)			
Cheese* (Per oz.: American, Bleu, Brie, Camembert, Cheddar, Colby, Feta, Fontina, Goat, Gouda, Gruyere, Mexican Queso, Monterey Jack, Mozzarella, Muenster, Parmesan, Pepper Jack, Provolone, Ricotta, Romano, Roquefort, String, Swiss)	90-125	Cream	
		Heavy	97
		Light	55
		Sour	54
		Cream Cheese (regular, fat free)	96/29
		Half & Half	36
		Milk (skim, 1%, 2%, whole)	40-75
Cottage Cheese (1/2 cup)	97	Yogurt (½ cup, plain only)	75
Caution Condiments (Check for sugars and use VERY sparingly)			
BBQ Sauce*	50-70	Steak Sauce* (1 Tbsp.)	15-35
Ketchup*	10-20	Tartar Sauce* (1 Tbsp.)	60-80
Mayonnaise* (1 Tbsp. Light or Regular)	35-100	Vinaigrette* (balsamic, barbeque, basil, Greek, herb, Italian, red wine)	25-80
Salad Dressings*	40-90		
Caution Fats & Oils (Limit to 1 ounce per serving)			
Bacon Grease	251	Oil (almond, avocado, canola, cashew, cocoa butter, cod, cod liver, cottonseed, flaxseed, ghee, grapeseed, hazelnut, lard, mustard, palm, peanut, safflower, salmon, sesame, soybean, walnut, wheat germ)	80-140
Butter	201		
Cooking Spray*	0-1		
Margarine (1 Tbsp.)	100		

ITEM	Cals/Oz.	ITEM	Cals/Oz.
Caution Beverages (Limit to ONE 5-oz. serving per day, consumed with a meal. One serving of wine counts as one of your daily caution foods. No dessert wines [port, sauternes, barsac, etc.])			
Red table wine (Burgundy, Cabernet, Zinfandel, Merlot, Pinot Noir, Shiraz, etc.)	127-145	White table wine (Chenin Blanc, Pinot Blanc/Grigio, Sauvignon Blanc, Chardonnay, Riesling, etc.)	121-150

* = check product label for calories

Once you have completed M1 and it has been a week or more since your last steak day, it's time to start adding carbohydrates. It's easy when you follow a few simple guidelines:

➤ Stick with whole, unprocessed foods.
➤ Include both protein and carbohydrates in your meals and snacks.
➤ Maintain your proper daily caloric intake based on your BMR.
➤ Weigh yourself daily.
➤ Proceed with caution after a steak day.
➤ Use the schedule below for adding carbs into your diet.

Week 1: One carbohydrate food per day, choosing a different food each day.

Week 2: Up to two carbohydrate foods per day, but not at the same meal.

Week 3: Start combining carbohydrate foods at the same protein-based meal once per day.

Best food choices to add during M2 are: brown rice, bananas, BBQ sauce, cornbread, whole grain crackers, frozen yogurt, garbanzo beans, grapes, gravy, grits, whole grain buns, honey, kidney beans, ketchup, legumes, lentils, melon, orange juice, pancakes, peas, popcorn, potatoes, steel-cut oatmeal, sweet potatoes, waffles, whole grain bread, whole grain cereals, whole wheat pasta, and yogurt. Alcoholic beverages may be consumed and count as one carb serving.

Once you have completed these last three weeks, you can start another round of the HCG protocol. Otherwise, you will be in Life Phase. The rules of Life Phase are: eat when you are hungry, stop when you are full, listen to what your body needs, weigh yourself every day and if you surpass your LDW by more than two pounds, do a steak day.

MAINTENANCE RECIPES
for the HCG Protocol

ALL OF THE MAINTENANCE RECIPES in this book have been carefully created to take advantage of the plethora of new foods allowed in this phase while maintaining your new weight. To meet your BMR calorie requirement in Maintenance, you need delicious, high calorie meals and snacks, which can be difficult without adding starches and sugars. There is no better source than this book for the delectable dishes you need to successfully complete this phase.

Most of these recipes offer an "M1 Caution Modification" and an "M2/Life Modification" for when you're ready to introduce caution foods, followed by starches and sugars, back into your meals. These modifications will keep you eating healthy while enjoying many of the foods you love. Be sure to follow the Maintenance guidelines to help your weight stabilize quickly and easily!

COLD DRINKS

MAINTENANCE

TERRIFICALLY REFRESHING and flavorful drinks await in the Maintenance phase of the HCG diet. With the expanded list of food and beverage selections, along with the exciting flavors of Capella and Stevia, you're in for a real treat when it comes to creating tasty and satisfying drinks.

Be sure to monitor both your "Caution" selections and calorie counts as you progress each week. Remember that the addition of alcohol, in any form, counts as a carbohydrate serving, preferably consumed only during the M2/Life phases. Be mindful of using only fresh fruit juices for all M1 recipes, as prepared juices almost always contain extra sugar even though the label doesn't show it.

Strawberry Kiwi Sangria, Vanilla Mint Mojito, Peachy Keen Quaff
(Recipes on pages 147–148)

Health Nut Cocktail

Muddling is the method bartenders use to obtain optimal flavor from ingredients. You can use a wooden spoon as a muddling stick, or simply crush the aromatics with a mortar and pestle.

1 thin slice fresh gingerroot	5 to 6 oz. vegetable juice (such as V-8)
1 small piece orange rind	Juice of 1 orange
1 Tbsp. fresh lime juice	Ice
6 drops Sweetleaf Stevia Valencia Orange	Orange slice for garnish

1. Place the ginger, orange rind, lime juice, and Stevia in a cocktail shaker and "muddle" until crushed and fragrant.
2. Add the vegetable juice, orange juice, and ice and shake until combined and well chilled.
3. Strain into a glass and serve garnished with the orange slice.

Makes 1 serving (82 calories; 1 gram protein, 18 grams carbohydrates)

M1 Caution Modification: Add ¼ cup carrot juice in Step 2.

M2/Life Modification: Add 1 shot vodka in Step 2.

Bloody Salsa Maria

For those who like it hot, here's a deliciously tangy version of a bloody Mary made with salsa and garnished with good-for-you veggies.

6 oz. tomato juice	Pinch celery salt
Juice of ½ lime	A skewer of fresh vegetables such as cherry tomatoes, cucumber and carrot rounds, and bell pepper slices for garnish.
6 drops Sweetleaf Stevia Valencia Orange	
Dash Frank's Hot Sauce	
1 Tbsp. prepared salsa, not chunky style	

Combine the drink ingredients in a tumbler and stir well. Add ice and garnish with the fresh vegetable skewer.

Makes 1 serving (60 calories; 10 grams carbohydrates)

M1 Caution Modification: Add ¼ cup orange juice.

M2/Life Modification: Add a shot of jalapeno-flavored vodka.

Blueberry Cobbler Delight

Years ago, cobbler cocktails were all the rage, making use of sweet, seasonal fruit for refreshing flavor. With a little help from Capella, you can enjoy this sweet treat any time of the year.

6 oz. club soda
1 Tbsp. lemon juice
4 to 6 drops Capella Blueberry
8 drops Clear Stevia, or more to taste

Crushed ice
¼ cup fresh blueberries, washed, stemmed, and lightly crushed

1. Combine the club soda, lemon juice, Capella, and Stevia in a tumbler, add the crushed ice, and stir well.
2. Stir in the blueberries and serve.

Makes 1 serving (30 calories; 8 grams carbohydrates)

M1 Caution Modification: Stir in 2 Tbsp. half & half and 6 drops Stevia Vanilla Crème.

M2/Life Modification: Add ¼ cup blueberry or blueberry/pomegranate juice.

Raspberry Sparkler

Enjoy this festive party drink during M1 and upgrade to a fabulous champagne cocktail in M2/Life.

6 oz. club soda
4 to 6 drops Capella Raspberry
8 drops Clear Stevia, or more to taste
3 or 4 fresh raspberries

Combine the club soda, Capella, and Stevia in a champagne flute. Top with the raspberries and serve.

Makes 1 serving (15 calories)

M1 Caution Modification: Add a splash of pink grapefruit juice.

M2/Life Modification: Replace the club soda with champagne.

Vanilla Mint Mojito

Here's a wonderfully refreshing "mocktail" made with the delicious flavors of Capella and Stevia that's easily upgraded to the real thing!

1 Tbsp. packed fresh mint leaves	4 to 6 drops Capella French Vanilla
1 thin lime slice	10 to 12 drops Clear Stevia
1 Tbsp. lemon juice	Crushed ice
4 to 6 drops Capella Cool Mint	Splash club soda
	Mint sprig for garnish

1. In a heavy-bottomed drinking glass, combine the mint, lime slice, lemon juice, Capella, and Stevia. Muddle (mash) until crushed and fragrant.
2. Add the ice, pour in the club soda, and stir well. Garnish with the mint sprig and serve.

Makes 1 serving (10 calories)

M1 Caution Modification: Add a splash of orange or grapefruit juice.

M2/Life Modification: Add a shot of rum.

Peachy Keen Quaff

The marvelous combination of peaches and cream makes this delicious drink a true delight to sip and savor.

½ cup unsweetened frozen peaches, diced	10 drops Clear Stevia, or more to taste
Juice of 1 orange	Crushed ice
4 to 6 drops Capella Peaches & Cream	Splash club soda

1. Combine the peaches, orange juice, Capella, and Stevia in a blender and puree until smooth. Transfer to a glass and add the crushed ice.
2. Top with a splash of club soda, taste for the addition of Stevia, and serve.

Makes 1 serving (70 calories; 1 gram protein, 16 grams carbohydrates)

M1 Caution Modification: Add 2 Tbsp. half & half to the blender.

M2/Life Modification: Substitute ⅓ cup peach nectar for the orange juice.

Strawberry Kiwi Sangria

Allowing the fruit to flavor the sangria overnight will also enhance its intoxicating fragrance and wonderful color.

1 pint water
15 drops Sweetleaf Stevia Grape
10 drops Sweetleaf Stevia Berry
½ lb. strawberries, stemmed, hulled, and sliced

1 large kiwi, peeled and diced
Splash club soda
Whole strawberries for garnish

1. In a small pitcher, combine all the ingredients except for the club soda, and stir well. Allow to chill overnight or for several hours in the refrigerator.
2. When ready to serve, taste for the addition of Stevia, pour into wine glasses, add a splash of club soda, and garnish with a strawberry.

Makes 2 servings (59 calories; 14 grams carbohydrates)

M1 Caution Modification: Add ½ cup halved seedless grapes to the fruit mixture.

M2/Life Modification: Substitute white wine for the water in Step 1.

Amaretto Sour

Here's a terrific sugar-free version of an old favorite that can be upgraded with a shot of whiskey for a great alternative to carb-laden liqueur cocktails.

Ice
1 Tbsp. fresh lime juice
2 Tbsp. fresh lemon juice
4 to 6 drops Capella Amaretto

10 to 12 drops Clear Stevia
Juice of ½ an orange
Splash club soda

Fill a wineglass with ice. Add the ingredients in the order listed, and stir well.

Makes 1 serving (50 calories; 12 grams carbohydrates)

M1 Caution Modification: Substitute grapefruit juice for the orange juice.

M2/Life Modification: Substitute a shot of whiskey for the orange juice.

Green Tea Spritzer

Perfect as a substitute for wine at dinnertime, this alcohol-free drink goes well with all types of food and is based on an easy-to-make VLCD beverage favorite.

½ cup boiling water
1 green tea bag
2 tsp. fresh lime juice

1 serving Real Ginger Ale (recipe page 3)
Sweetleaf Stevia Lemon Drop to taste

1. Steep the tea in the boiling water for 10 minutes. Remove the tea bag and set the liquid aside to cool.
2. In a wineglass with ice, combine the steeped tea, lime juice, and ginger ale and stir. Add the Stevia Lemon Drop to taste and serve.

Makes 1 serving (5 calories)

M1 Caution Modification: Add a splash of aloe vera juice.

M2/Life Modification: Add a splash of white wine or no-sugar-added white grape juice.

Creamy Holiday Eggnog

It wouldn't be the holidays without a glass of eggnog, and thanks to Capella and Stevia, you can toast along with your guests with this delightful version.

1 cup unsweetened plain almond milk
4 or 5 drops Capella Italian Egg Nog
10 to 12 drops Clear Stevia

1 egg white
Pinch cream of tartar
Dash ground nutmeg

1. Combine the almond milk, Capella, and Stevia in a small bowl and whisk to combine. Taste for sweetness and adjust as necessary.
2. In another small bowl, beat or whisk the egg white with the cream of tartar to soft peaks. Carefully fold into the milk mixture until combined.
3. Pour into a glass, finish with a dash of nutmeg and serve immediately.

Makes 1 serving (56 calories; 2 grams fat, 7 grams protein, 2 grams carbohydrates)

M1 Modification: Replace almond milk with half & half or whole milk.

M2/Life Modification: Top with a dollop of whipped cream.

HOT DRINKS

WARM, ROBUSTLY FLAVORED, and delectably satisfying, the hot drinks in this chapter fit into the Maintenance food plan and are all made easily and quickly with the help of Capella and Stevia flavor drops. Whether it's a coffee or tea drink you're after, or a marvelous chocolate beverage to sip, you'll find what you're looking for here.

Be sure to monitor both your "Caution" selections and calorie counts as you progress each week. Remember that the addition of alcohol, in any form, counts as a carbohydrate serving, preferably consumed only during the M2/Life phases. Be sure to use "unsweetened" cocoa powder, not "sugar-free" cocoa, which may contain other types of unacceptable sweeteners as well as unwanted chemical additives and preservatives.

Chocolate Coconut Almond Delight
(Recipe on page 157)

Tangerine Cinnamon Tea

This soothing hot brew will make you feel cozy and comfy while the delicious aromas waft through the house.

Juice of 2 tangerines
1 small cinnamon stick
6 drops Sweetleaf Stevia
  Valencia Orange

3 drops Sweetleaf Stevia
  Lemon Drop
1 tea bag, black or orange pekoe
½ cup boiling water
Clear Stevia drops to taste

1. In a small saucepan, combine the fresh tangerine juice, cinnamon, and Stevia. Stir well and bring just to a simmer over medium-low heat. Set aside.
2. Steep the tea in the water in a mug for 2 to 3 minutes and remove the bag. Stir in the tangerine mixture, add Clear Stevia to taste, and serve.

Makes 1 serving (60 calories; 10 grams carbohydrates)

M1 Caution Modification: Stir 2 Tbsp. pureed mango into the tangerine mixture when heating.

M2/Life Modification: Add a shot of Grand Marnier.

Fresh Raspberry Tisane

Typically herbal and fruity, tisanes can be quite refreshing and energizing when sipped on an afternoon break with a snack.

1 raspberry herbal tea bag
1 cup boiling water
¼ cup pureed fresh or frozen
  (no sugar added) raspberries

1 tsp. lemon juice
4 drops Capella Raspberry
8 to 10 drops Clear Stevia

1. Steep the tea bag in the water for 3 to 5 minutes and discard the bag. Meanwhile, heat the pureed raspberries with the lemon juice and Capella in a small saucepan or in the microwave.
2. Stir the raspberry mixture into the steeped tea, add Clear Stevia to taste, and serve.

Makes 1 serving (25 calories; 4 grams carbohydrates)

M1 Caution Modification: Add a splash of milk or half & half.

M2/Life Modification: Add 2 Tbsp. raspberry liqueur.

Pumpkin Chai

Exotic chai is the perfect comfort drink when the weather turns chilly. Try also making this with a pumpkin-scented coffee as the base.

1 cup unsweetened plain soy milk or almond milk

1 tea bag, black or orange pekoe

1 cinnamon stick

4 whole black peppercorns

4 or 5 drops Capella Pumpkin Pie Spice

10 to 12 drops Clear Stevia

1. Bring soy/almond milk just to a boil in a small saucepan. Remove from heat and stir in tea bag, cinnamon, peppercorns, Capella, and Stevia.
2. Keep warm and allow to steep for 5 minutes.
3. Strain and serve.

Makes 1 serving (Soy milk: 80 calories; almond milk: 40 calories; 4 grams fat, 7 grams protein, 4 grams carbohydrates)

M1 Caution Modification: Replace soy/almond milk with half & half or whole milk.

M2/Life Modification: Top with whipped cream and a drizzle of maple syrup.

Gingerbread Chai

Almond milk provides the richness, while adding a unique and delightful flavor, to this version of chai made with black tea.

1 cup unsweetened plain almond milk

1 tea bag, black or orange pekoe

2 whole cloves

1 cinnamon stick

4 whole black peppercorns

4 or 5 drops Capella Gingerbread

10 to 12 drops Clear Stevia

1. Bring almond milk just to a boil in a small saucepan. Remove from heat and stir in tea bag, cloves, cinnamon, peppercorns, Capella, and Stevia.
2. Keep warm and allow to steep for 5 minutes.
3. Strain and serve.

Makes 1 serving (40 calories; 4 grams fat, 7 grams protein, 4 grams carbohydrates)

M1 Caution Modification: Replace almond milk with half & half or whole milk.

M2/Life Modification: Top with whipped cream and a drizzle of caramel syrup.

Caramel Latte

Delicious caramel kicks up this great morning or afternoon coffee while almond milk adds good protein and nourishment.

1 cup unsweetened plain almond milk

1 cup hot fresh brewed coffee

6 to 8 drops Capella Caramel

Clear Stevia drops to taste

Combine all the ingredients in a medium saucepan and bring just to a boil, whisking until piping hot. Pour into a large café au lait cup and serve.

Makes 1 serving (40 calories; 4 grams fat, 7 grams protein, 4 grams carbohydrates)

M1 Caution Modification: Replace half the almond milk with whole milk or half & half.

M2/Life Modification: Add a dollop of whipped cream and a drizzle of caramel syrup.

Toasted Marshmallow Cappuccino

With the flavor of toasted marshmallows, this pick-me-up cup of flavor will become a real favorite.

4 oz. hot strong coffee or espresso

3 oz. almond milk

3 drops Capella Marshmallow

2 drops Capella Pralines & Cream

Clear Stevia drops to taste

1. Have ready a cup of hot coffee or espresso. In a small saucepan, heat just to boiling the milk and Capella, whisking a bit to create foam.
2. Pour immediately into the coffee cup, sweeten with Clear Stevia to taste, and serve.

Makes 1 serving (20 calories; 1 gram fat, 1 gram protein, 1 gram carbohydrates)

M1 Modification: Replace almond milk with light or heavy cream.

M2/Life Modification: Sweeten with a combination of Stevia and raw sugar.

Spiced Almond Milk

The intoxicating combination of flavors and spices in this wonderful toasty warm drink will delight and surprise you with each sip.

1 cup unsweetened almond milk
3 drops Capella Amaretto
3 drops Capella Irish Cream
8 drops Clear Stevia, or more to taste

Pinch ground cinnamon
Pinch ground cloves
Pinch ground cardamom

Combine all the ingredients in a small saucepan and bring just to a simmer over medium heat, whisking occasionally. Pour into a mug and serve.

Makes 1 serving (40 calories; 3 grams fat, 1 gram protein, 2 grams carbohydrates)

M1 Caution Modification: Top with a dollop of whipped cream sweetened with Stevia.

M2/Life Modification: Add 2 Tbsp. Amaretto liqueur.

French Vanilla Café

The delicious flavor of vanilla teams up with creamy almond milk to make a coffee treat that's sure to please.

½ cup unsweetened almond milk
3 to 5 drops Capella French Vanilla

⅔ cup hot fresh brewed coffee
Clear Stevia drops to taste

In a small saucepan, heat the almond milk with the Capella. Pour into a mug containing the hot coffee, sweeten with Clear Stevia to taste, and serve.

Makes 1 serving (20 calories; 3 grams fat, 1 gram protein, 2 grams carbohydrates)

M1 Caution Modification: Replace the almond milk with half & half or whole milk.

M2/Life Modification: Add a shot of Kahlua and top with whipped cream.

Chocolate Coconut Almond Delight

Three yummy flavors that go together so well make for this warm and wonderful treat that's good enough for dessert.

1 cup unsweetened almond milk
1 Tbsp. unsweetened cocoa
powder

4 to 6 drops Capella Chocolate
Coconut Almond
12 or more drops Clear Stevia

Combine all the ingredients in a small saucepan and warm just to a boil over medium heat, whisking occasionally. Pour into a mug and serve. Garnish with cinnamon stick.

Makes 1 serving (60 calories; 3 grams fat, 2 grams protein, 5 grams carbohydrates)

M1 Caution Modification: Substitute half the almond milk with half & half.

M2/Life Modification: Top with a dollop of whipped cream and a few sliced almonds.

Melted Peppermint Patty

Chocolate and mint are always great partners and here they join up for a wonderful creamy creation made with almond milk and flavorful Capella drops.

1 cup unsweetened plain almond milk
1½ Tbsp. unsweetened cocoa powder
3 to 5 drops Capella Dutch Chocolate
Mint

12 drops Clear Stevia, or more
to taste
Mint sprig for garnish

Combine all the ingredients, except for the mint sprig, in a small saucepan and bring just to a boil over medium heat, whisking occasionally. Pour into a mug, garnish with the mint sprig, and serve.

Makes 1 serving (70 calories; 4 grams fat, 8 grams protein, 7 grams carbohydrates)

M1 Caution Modification: Replace the almond milk with whole milk.

M2/Life Modification: Top with marshmallows.

SMOOTHIES AND PROTEIN SHAKES

IT CAN BE CHALLENGING to consume enough calories and grams of protein needed to maintain your weight loss in M1 as your body works to stabilize its new weight. These delicious and protein-rich smoothies and shakes are just the solution to reaching your daily calorie and protein goals.

Don't be afraid to be creative with the wide variety of Capella and Stevia flavors. Mix and match and make your own favorite! Be sure to monitor both your "Caution" selections and calorie counts as you progress each week.

Apricot Blackberry Smoothie
(Recipe on page 162)

Super Protein Hot Chocolate Café

Enjoy a rich and nourishing hot drink at breakfast or snack time that's full of chocolately flavor and packed with protein.

4 oz. unsweetened plain almond milk, heated

1 packet (25.5 grams) 0–5 carb Chocolate whey protein powder

Splash hot fresh brewed coffee

3 drops Capella Chocolate Fudge Brownie

2 drops Capella Cappuccino

Clear Stevia drops to taste

Whisk together the almond milk, whey, coffee, and Capella in a small bowl or combine in a shaker or blender until smooth. Pour into a mug, sweeten with Stevia, and serve.

Makes 1 serving (77 calories; 3 grams fat, 21 grams protein, 3.5 grams carbohydrates)

M1 Caution Modification: Stir in a splash of half & half.

M2/Life Modification: Replace almond milk with chocolate almond milk.

Raspberry Vanilla "White" Chocolate Protein Power

This great tasting and terrifically nourishing hot breakfast or snack protein drink will become a favorite for life!

4 oz. unsweetened plain almond milk, heated

1 packet (25.5 grams) 0–5 carb Vanilla whey protein powder

6 to 8 drops Sweetleaf Stevia Chocolate

3 or 4 drops Capella Raspberry

3 or 4 drops Clear Stevia

Whisk together the almond milk, whey, Stevia, and Capella in a small bowl or combine in a shaker or blender until smooth. Pour into a mug, sweeten with Stevia, and serve.

Makes 1 serving (77 calories; 3 grams fat, 21 grams protein, 3.5 grams carbohydrates)

M1 Caution Modification: Stir in a splash of half & half.

M2/Life Modification: Add 1 oz. melted white chocolate to the blender.

Praline Vanilla Protein Shake

Creamy, warm, and flavorful, you'll get a powerful punch of protein as well in this deliciously unique shake.

4 oz. unsweetened plain almond milk, heated	5 or 6 drops Capella Pralines & Cream
1 packet (25.5 grams) 0–5 carb Vanilla whey protein powder	3 or 4 drops Clear Stevia

Whisk together the almond milk, whey, and Capella in a small bowl or combine in a shaker or blender until smooth. Pour into a mug, sweeten with Stevia, and serve.

Makes 1 serving (77 calories; 3 grams fat, 21 grams protein, 3.5 grams carbohydrates)

M1 Caution Modification: Stir in a splash of half & half.

M2/Life Modification: Top with whipped cream and chopped nuts.

Apricot Blackberry Smoothie

Both fruity and creamy, you'll enjoy the refreshing combination of flavors in this healthy smoothie that's perfect for any time of day.

1 cup unsweetened plain almond milk, well chilled	2 Tbsp. crushed ice
1/3 cup fresh apricots, diced	8 to 10 drops Sweetleaf Stevia Apricot Nectar
1/3 cup frozen blackberries	Clear Stevia to taste

Combine all the ingredients in a blender and puree until smooth. Pour into a tumbler, taste for additional sweetness, and serve.

Makes 1 serving (120 calories; 4 grams fat, 8 grams protein, 18 grams carbohydrates)

M1 Caution Modification: Add a splash of half & half.

M2/Life Modification: Add 1/3 cup apricot juice.

Strawberries and Cream Smoothie

Who can resist the sweet flavor of ripe strawberries with the silky smoothness of cream? Keep fresh strawberry pieces in the freezer for handy smoothie-making without the need for ice.

1 cup fresh or frozen strawberry pieces

½ cup unsweetened plain almond milk, well chilled

¼ cup crushed ice

4 to 6 drops Capella Strawberries & Cream

4 drops Sweetleaf Stevia Berry

10 drops Clear Stevia, or more to taste

Combine all the ingredients in a blender and puree until smooth. Pour into a tumbler, taste for additional sweetness, and serve.

Makes 1 serving (70 calories; 2 grams fat, 4 grams protein, 15 grams carbohydrates)

M1 Caution Modification: Replace half the almond milk with light cream or plain yogurt.

M2/Life Modification: Add ½ a banana and ¼ cup half & half.

Double Almond Chocolate Shake

Almond milk adds great flavor and consistency in this delicious shake that can be made with or without a boost of chocolate protein powder.

1 cup unsweetened almond milk, chilled

1½ Tbsp. unsweetened cocoa powder

¼ cup crushed ice

3 to 5 drops Capella Amaretto

8 drops Sweetleaf Stevia Chocolate

Clear Stevia drops to taste

½ packet (12.75 grams) 0–5 carb Chocolate whey protein powder (optional)

Combine all the ingredients in a blender and puree until smooth. Pour into a tumbler and taste for the addition of Clear Stevia before serving.

Makes 1 serving (with 0–5 carb whey protein powder: 110 calories; 2 grams fat, 14 grams protein, 8 grams carbohydrates)

M1 Caution Modification: Add a splash of light cream.

M2/Life Modification: Replace half the almond milk with chocolate almond milk.

Nutty Vanilla Protein Shake

If you're nuts for the flavor of nuts, this delicious and nourishing shake is for you. Try adding different nuts during M2/Life for wonderful variety.

1 cup unsweetened almond milk, well chilled

¼ cup crushed ice

6 to 8 drops Sweetleaf Stevia Hazelnut

1 packet (25.5 grams) 0–5 carb Vanilla whey protein powder

Clear Stevia drops to taste

Combine all the ingredients in a blender and puree until smooth. Pour into a tumbler and taste for the addition of Clear Stevia before serving.

Makes 1 serving (125 calories; 4 grams fat, 23 grams protein, 5 grams carbohydrates)

M1 Caution Modification: Add a splash of half & half or light cream.

M2/Life Modification: Replace almond milk with vanilla almond milk and add 1 Tbsp. chopped almonds or hazelnuts.

Banana Date Nut Shake (Two Caution Ingredients)

Naturally sweet bananas and dates get an added boost of flavor from Capella and Stevia in this creamy, healthy shake made with almond milk.

1 cup frozen banana pieces

1 cup pitted dates

1 cup almond milk

2 Tablespoons walnuts

3 to 5 drops Capella Banana

12 to 15 drops Clear Stevia

Combine all the ingredients in a blender and puree until smooth. Pour and serve immediately.

Makes two servings. (265 calories; 4 grams protein, 28 grams carbs)

BREAKFAST

A FTER STICKING TO THE STRICT protocol in VLCD, these terrific ideas for the first meal of the day in Maintenance will no
doubt tickle your taste buds. From delicious omelets to creative
fruit treats, you'll delight in the variety of options, thanks to the
flavors of Capella and Stevia. You'll also find some griddle favorites that will make you think twice about ever eating bread again!

Be sure to monitor both your "Caution" selections and calorie
counts as you progress each week. Only introduce sugars and
starches when allowed. Although the calorie counts given are as
accurate as possible, please consult the nutritional labels of the
specific products used to be sure.

Sweet Strawberry Pancakes
(Recipe on page 175)

Eggs Galore

Peaches and Cream Omelet

Peaches, cream, and almonds are classic companions and here they come together for a delicious sweet omelet that's sure to start your day off right.

½ medium peach, diced	8 to 10 drops Clear Stevia
2 Tbsp. whipped cottage cheese	2 large eggs
1 Tbsp. unsweetened almond milk	1 Tbsp. water
3 or 4 drops Capella Peaches & Cream	Pinch salt
2 or 3 drops Capella Amaretto	1 tsp. olive or coconut oil

1. In a small bowl, combine the peach, cottage cheese, almond milk, Capella, and Stevia and stir well to combine. Set aside.
2. In another bowl, whisk together the eggs, water, and salt.
3. Heat the oil in a medium-sized nonstick skillet and pour in the egg mixture. Spread evenly in pan, cover, reduce heat to very low, and cook until just set, about 2 minutes.
4. Spread the peach mixture over one side of the omelet and carefully flip over. Cook another minute, then transfer to a plate and serve.

Makes 1 serving (225 calories; 14 grams fat, 8 grams protein, 7 grams carbohydrates)

M1 Caution Modification: Replace the cottage cheese with goat cheese and the almond milk with light cream.

M2/Life Modification: Top with a dollop of Stevia-sweetened whipped cream and some toasted sliced almonds.

Breakfast Soufflé with Apples and Cinnamon

Light, airy, and delicious, this easy-to-make dish is irresistible with the sweet fragrance of warm apples and cinnamon.

¾ cup unsweetened applesauce
4 to 6 drops Sweetleaf Stevia Cinnamon
½ small apple, peeled, cored, and diced

1 large egg, separated
2 Tbsp. whipped cottage cheese
3 drops Capella Apple Pie
6 drops Clear Stevia
2 large egg whites

1. Preheat the oven to 350° F. Spread 2 Tbsp. of the applesauce over the bottom of each of two 12-oz. ramekins or baking dishes and set aside.
2. In a small bowl, combine the remaining applesauce, Stevia Cinnamon drops, and diced apple. In a large bowl, whisk together the egg yolk, cottage cheese, Capella drops, and Stevia. Add the diced apple mixture to the egg yolk mixture and stir well to combine.
3. In a medium bowl, beat the 3 egg whites until stiff peaks form. Mix half the beaten egg whites into the apple mixture, then gently fold the remaining beaten egg whites into the mixture, maintaining as much volume as possible.
4. Divide the mixture between the 2 ramekins and smooth the top over with the back of a spoon. Bake on a cookie sheet until puffed and browned, 15 to 20 minutes, and serve immediately.

Makes 2 servings (125 calories; 3 grams fat, 8 grams protein, 15 grams carbohydrates)

M1 Caution Modification: Add 1 Tbsp. golden raisins to the bottom of each soufflé before adding the egg mixture.

M2/Life Modification: Lightly butter the bottom of the ramekins and replace the applesauce on the bottom with graham cracker crumbs.

Banana and Peanut Butter Frittata

Although the actual banana and peanut butter aren't added until the modification versions, thanks to Capella and Stevia the delicious flavors are there for a wonderful morning treat.

2 large eggs
2 Tbsp. unsweetened almond milk
¼ cup whipped cottage cheese
4 drops Capella Banana

4 drops Capella Peanut Butter
8 drops Clear Stevia
1 tsp. olive or coconut oil

1. In a medium bowl, whisk together the eggs and almond milk. In another bowl, combine the cottage cheese, Capella, and Stevia.
2. Coat the bottom and sides of a medium nonstick skillet with the oil and heat over medium heat. Pour in the egg mixture and tilt the pan to distribute evenly. Cover, reduce the heat to low, and cook until just set, about 2 minutes.
3. Spread the cottage cheese mixture on one side, fold over, and transfer to a dish. Serve immediately.

Makes 1 serving (240 calories; 17 grams fat, 19 grams protein, 2 grams carbohydrates)

M1 Caution Modification: Add ¼ cup diced banana to the cottage cheese mixture.

M2/Life Modification: Replace the cottage cheese with 2 Tbsp. cream cheese and 2 Tbsp. peanut butter whipped together, along with the diced banana.

Maple Bacon and Egg Scramble

The delicious flavor of maple enhances this delightful scramble that's perfect for a quick morning meal.

2 slices cooked turkey bacon, crumbled

2 large eggs

1 Tbsp. almond milk

3 to 5 drops Capella French Toast

6 drops Clear Stevia

½ tsp. olive or coconut oil

1. In a small bowl, whisk together the eggs, almond milk, Capella, and Stevia.
2. Lightly coat the bottom and sides of a medium nonstick skillet with the oil and heat over medium heat. Pour in the egg mixture, add the bacon, and scramble until just set, 1 to 2 minutes. Transfer to a plate and serve.

Makes 1 serving (212 calories; 15 grams fat, 16 grams protein)

M1 Caution Modification: Stir in 1 oz. diced brie cheese just before serving.

M2/Life Modification: Serve in a low-carb multigrain wrap.

Eggs à la Benedict

Enjoy this mock version of eggs benedict during M1 and delight in the real thing during M2/Life Maintenance.

¼ cup cottage cheese

2 Tbsp. unsweetened almond milk

6 drops Sweetleaf Stevia Lemon Drop

Fresh ground pepper

2 slices Canadian bacon, heated

2 large eggs, poached and kept warm

Pinch fresh parsley, chopped

1. In a small saucepan over low heat, whisk together the cottage cheese, almond milk, Stevia, and pepper until smooth and warm, but not bubbly.
2. Arrange the bacon slices on a warm plate, top each with a poached egg, spoon the sauce mixture over everything, and top with the chopped parsley. Serve immediately.

Makes 1 serving (290 calories; 16 grams fat, 31 grams protein, 3 grams carbohydrates)

M1 Caution Modification: Replace the cottage cheese sauce with 2 Tbsp. hollandaise sauce flavored with Stevia Lemon Drop.

M2/Life Modification: Serve each bacon slice and egg on top of light, whole-grain English muffin halves.

Super Smoked Salmon Scramble

A host of delicious flavors come together in this satisfying scramble that's as easy to make as it is to eat.

1 tsp. olive or coconut oil
½ small onion, thinly sliced
1 tsp. capers, drained
¼ cup artichoke hearts, roughly chopped
¼ tsp. lemon zest

1 oz. smoked salmon, roughly chopped
2 large eggs, beaten
2 Tbsp. cottage cheese
6 drops Sweetleaf Stevia Lemon Drop
Fresh ground pepper

1. Heat the olive oil in a medium nonstick skillet over medium heat. Add the onion and sauté until softened, about 3 minutes. Add the capers, lemon zest, and salmon, stir well, and cook another minute.
2. Pour in the eggs, reduce the heat to low, and scramble, constantly stirring, until just set. Transfer to a warm plate.
3. In a small bowl, stir together the cottage cheese, Stevia, and pepper, and spoon on top of the cooked eggs. Serve immediately.

Makes 1 serving (290 calories; 16 grams fat, 19 grams protein, 11 grams carbohydrates)

M1 Caution Modification: Replace the cottage cheese with whipped cream cheese mixed with 1 Tbsp. light cream.

M2/Life Modification: Serve over 1 slice of toasted rye bread.

Fruity Favorites

Blackberry and Peach Compote

Warm, sweet, and delicious, this easy-to-make fruit dish is fabulous on its own or in M2/Life as a topping for nourishing hot cereal.

½ cup peaches, diced
1 tsp. lemon juice
1 Tbsp. water
3 to 5 drops Capella Peaches & Cream

8 drops Clear Stevia
½ cup blackberries
Almond milk (optional)

1. In a medium saucepan, combine the peaches, lemon juice, water, Capella, and Stevia. Bring to a simmer over medium heat and cook, stirring often, just until the peaches begin to break down, about 5 minutes. Stir in the blackberries and cook over low heat for a minute more.
2. To serve, transfer to a bowl, and pour a little almond milk around the edge, if desired.

Makes 1 serving (30 calories; 1 gram protein, 15 grams carbohydrates)

M1 Caution Modification: Serve over ½ cup plain nonfat yogurt.

M2/Life Modification: Serve over ½ cup hot cereal with a drizzle of milk.

Tropical Fruit Cup

The refreshing fruits of the tropics get a bit of extra sweetness and flavor from Capella and Stevia in this terrific start to the morning.

4 small strawberries
½ kiwi, peeled and diced
½ cup papaya chunks
¼ cup pineapple, diced

1 Clementine orange, peeled and segmented
6 to 8 drops Capella with Stevia Piña Colada

In a small bowl, gently toss together all the ingredients and set aside for 10 minutes before serving, or chill overnight.

Makes 2 servings (55 calories; 14 grams carbohydrates)

M1 Caution Modification: Add ½ cup sliced banana or mango chunks.

M2/Life Modification: Serve over ⅔ cup nonfat Greek yogurt and sprinkle with toasted shredded coconut.

French Vanilla Parfait with Raspberries

Make these ahead and have on hand for a quick sweet breakfast treat to have after scrambled or boiled eggs.

1 cup whipped cottage cheese
2 Tbsp. unsweetened almond milk
4 or 5 drops Capella French Vanilla
6 drops Clear Stevia, or more to taste

1 cup fresh raspberries
6 or 8 drops Sweetleaf Stevia Berry
Mint sprigs for garnish

1. In a medium bowl, whisk together the cottage cheese, almond milk, Capella, and Clear Stevia until smooth. In a small bowl, toss together the fresh raspberries and Stevia Berry.
2. Decoratively layer the cheese mixture and raspberry mixture in two parfait glasses or champagne flutes and chill. Garnish with the mint sprigs before serving.

Makes 2 servings (130 calories; 3 grams fat, 14 grams protein, 12 grams carbohydrates)

M1 Caution Modification: Replace the cottage cheese with plain yogurt and eliminate the almond milk.

M2/Life Modification: Sprinkle ½ cup granola while layering along with the raspberries.

Strawberries and "Cream" Breakfast Cup

Almost as good as the real deal, this delightful morning fruit cup is both refreshing and light.

1 cup strawberries, stemmed
  and diced

1 Tbsp. water

3 to 5 drops Capella Strawberries
  & Cream

8 drops Clear Stevia, or more to
  taste

½ cup whipped cottage cheese

3 to 5 drops Capella French Vanilla

¼ tsp. flax seeds

1. In a small bowl, gently stir together the strawberries, water, Capella, and Clear Stevia. Set aside for 10 to 15 minutes.
2. In another small bowl, whisk together the cottage cheese, Stevia Vanilla, and flax seeds.
3. To serve, gently fold the strawberry mixture into the cheese mixture and spoon into a dish.

Makes 1 serving (150 calories; 3 grams fat, 14 grams protein, 17 grams carbohydrates)

M1 Caution Modification: Replace the cottage cheese with light sour cream.

M2/Life Modification: Replace the cottage cheese with whipped heavy cream, eliminate the flax seeds, and top with toasted wheat germ.

From the Griddle

Sweet Strawberry Pancakes

A terrific treat for breakfast or brunch, these easy to make griddle cakes will delight everyone's taste buds!

For the Pancakes:
¼ cup 0–5 carb Vanilla whey protein powder
1½ tsp. baking powder
2 large eggs, slightly beaten
2 tsp. coconut or light olive oil
6 to 8 drops Capella Sweet Strawberry
15 drops Clear Stevia, or more to taste
2 Tbsp. almond milk

For the Strawberry Syrup:
1 cup strawberries, diced
$\frac{1}{3}$ cup water
3 or 4 drops Capella Sweet Strawberry
Clear Stevia drops to taste

1. In a small bowl, stir together the protein powder and baking powder. In another small bowl stir together the remaining pancake ingredients. Combine the wet and dry ingredients together, stirring with a fork, and set aside.
2. In a small saucepan, combine the syrup ingredients and bring to a simmer over medium heat. Cook, stirring often, until strawberries soften and form a syrup. Set aside and keep warm.
3. Heat a nonstick pan or griddle and lightly oil to prevent sticking. Divide the mixture into 4 pancake mounds and cook until golden on both sides, turning when bubbles appear around the edges. Serve immediately with the strawberry syrup on top.

Makes 2 servings (190 calories; 7 grams fat, 15 grams protein, 7 grams carbohydrates)

M1 Caution Modification: Replace the oil in the pancake recipe with the same amount of melted butter.

M2/Life Modification: Add 1 Tbsp. of strawberry jam, no sugar added, to the syrup when cooking.

Cinnamon Danish Pancakes

If you're missing the comfort of breakfast griddle treats, these easy-to-make pancakes will definitely fill the void. Try substituting different flavors of Capella and Stevia for variety.

2 Tbsp. 0–5 carb Vanilla whey protein powder
¾ tsp. baking powder
½ tsp. ground cinnamon
Dash ground nutmeg
Dash ground ginger
1 large egg, slightly beaten

1 tsp. coconut or light olive oil
6 drops Capella Cinnamon Danish Swirl
15 drops Clear Stevia, or more to taste
1 Tbsp. water or almond milk

1. In a small bowl, stir together the protein powder, baking powder, and spices. In another small bowl, stir together the remaining ingredients. Combine the wet and dry ingredients together, stirring with a fork, and set aside.
2. Heat a nonstick pan or griddle and lightly oil to prevent sticking. Divide the mixture into 2 pancake mounds and cook until golden on both sides, turning when bubbles appear around the edges. Serve immediately.

Makes 1 serving (165 calories; 18 grams fat, 11 grams protein, 3 grams carbohydrates)

M1 Caution Modification: Top with 1 tsp. of butter or cream cheese.

M2/Life Modification: Drizzle a small amount of maple or other syrup over the top.

SOUPS AND SALADS

SOOTHING SOUPS AND SATISFYING SALADS continue to be great choices during the Maintenance phase of the HCG Protocol. Here the possibilities are broadened with the addition of many more allowable ingredients. Capella and Stevia are added to enhance and sweeten many selections that might normally call for sugars and/or starches with remarkably delectable results.

As with all Maintenance recipes, monitor both your "Caution" selections and calorie counts as you progress each week. Be sure to only introduce your allotted sugars and starches when allowed. Although the calorie counts given are as accurate as possible, when using specific products, please consult the nutritional labels to be sure.

Silky Shrimp Bisque
(Recipe on page 181)

The Soup Bowl

Creamy Broccoli Soup

Nutritious broccoli is featured in this smooth and creamy soup with a hint of zesty lemon and a cheddar-cheese upgrade.

1½ lb. broccoli, cut into florets and pieces

1 medium onion, roughly chopped

3 cups Basic Chicken or Vegetable Broth (see page 21 or 22)

Dash paprika

12 drops Sweetleaf Stevia Lemon Drop

1 cup unsweetened plain almond milk

Salt and pepper to taste

1. In a large soup pot, combine the broccoli, onion, broth, paprika, and Stevia. Bring the broccoli mixture to a boil, reduce the heat to low, and simmer until the vegetables are tender, about 25 minutes.
2. Add the almond milk to the soup pot and continue cooking for 2 minutes. Remove from the heat and begin ladling into a blender. Working in batches, blend until smooth and transfer to a clean saucepan.
3. Reheat the blended soup and season to taste with salt and pepper before serving.

Makes 4 servings (90 calories; 2 grams fat, 6 grams protein, 13 grams carbohydrates)

M1 Caution Modification: Top each serving with 1 oz. shredded cheddar cheese.

M2/Life Modification: Top with cheese and croutons or crumbled crackers.

Tomato Florentine Soup

Sweet and flavorful San Marzano tomatoes and a surprising addition of Stevia highlight this terrific soup with the Florentine touch of nutritious spinach and a hint of fragrant basil.

2 28-oz. cans plum tomatoes, no sugar

2 Tbsp. extra virgin olive oil

1 medium onion, peeled and finely chopped

Salt and pepper to taste

¼ tsp. dried oregano

1 cup Basic Chicken or Vegetable Broth (see page 21 or 22)

10 drops Sweetleaf Stevia Grape

10-oz. package frozen chopped spinach, thawed and squeezed dry

½ cup unsweetened plain almond milk

2 Tbsp. fresh basil, chopped

1. Working in batches, process the canned tomatoes and their juices in a food processor fitted with a steel blade until smooth. Set aside.
2. Heat the olive oil in a soup pot over medium heat. Add the chopped onion, salt, pepper, and oregano, and cook, stirring often, until softened but not brown, about 4 minutes.
3. Pour in the processed tomatoes, broth, and Stevia, and bring the mixture to a low boil over medium heat, simmering for 10 minutes.
4. Stir in the spinach and almond milk and continue to cook for 3 to 5 minutes. Taste for the addition of salt and pepper. To serve, ladle into soup bowls and top with chopped basil.

Makes 4 servings (160 calories; 7.5 grams fat, 4 grams protein, 16 grams carbohydrates)

M1 Caution Modification: Replace the almond milk with light cream.

M2/Life Modification: Stir in 1 cup cooked small pasta such as ditalini before serving.

Silky Shrimp Bisque

Smooth as silk and full of flavor, this elegant dish is a terrific start to a light lunch or dinner.

1 Tbsp. olive oil

1 medium leek, white part only, roughly chopped

½ medium fennel bulb, trimmed and roughly chopped

1 medium carrot, roughly chopped

1 bottle (8 oz.) clam juice

3 cups water

Juice of 1 orange

8 drops Sweetleaf Stevia Valencia Orange

2 Tbsp. tomato paste

1 lb. large, uncooked shrimp, peeled and deveined

½ cup unsweetened plain almond milk

1 tsp. fresh lemon juice

Salt and pepper to taste

1. Heat oil in a soup pot over medium heat and add the leek, fennel, and carrot. Cook over medium-low heat without browning, stirring occasionally, for 5 minutes.
2. Stir in clam juice, water, orange juice, Stevia, and tomato paste and bring to a simmer. Stir in the shrimp and cook, covered, at a low simmer, stirring occasionally, for 25 minutes. Stir in almond milk and cook uncovered 2 minutes more.
3. Working in batches, puree bisque in a blender and return to pot. Add lemon juice, season with salt and pepper, and serve immediately.

Makes 4 servings (190 calories; 4 grams fat, 25 grams protein, 11 grams carbohydrates)

M1 Caution Modification: Replace the almond milk with light cream.

M2/Life Modification: Add 2 Tbsp. Pernod, or other anise-flavored liqueur, before blending.

Creamy Chicken Chowder

Easy to make and delectable to eat, this rich-tasting soup gets a subtle flavor boost from a surprising source.

2 strips turkey bacon, diced
1 tsp. olive oil
1 medium onion, diced
1 medium celery stalk, diced
1 medium red bell pepper, seeded and diced
Salt to taste
$\frac{1}{8}$ tsp. cayenne pepper, or more to taste

4 cups Basic Chicken Broth (see page 21)
2 cups chicken breast, cooked and diced
1 cup unsweetened almond milk
5 drops Capella Amaretto
6 to 8 drops Clear Stevia
1 tsp. fresh parsley, finely chopped

1. Fry the bacon in the oil in a heavy pot over medium heat, stirring often, until crisp. Remove bacon with a slotted spoon and drain on paper towels.
2. Add the onion, celery, bell pepper, salt, and cayenne pepper and cook over medium heat, stirring often, until vegetables are soft but not browned, about 5 minutes. Pour in the broth and bring to a boil. Reduce the heat to low and add the diced chicken. Cook on a low simmer, stirring occasionally, for 10 minutes.
3. Stir in the almond milk, Capella, and Stevia and continue to cook for 3 minutes. Remove from the heat. Transfer half the soup to a blender and puree until smooth. Return to the pot and stir into the remaining soup for a creamy but still chunky consistency.
4. Taste for seasoning and serve piping hot sprinkled with the bacon bits and parsley.

Makes 4 servings (200 calories; 6 grams fat, 18 grams protein, 8 grams carbohydrates)

M1 Caution Modification: Serve sprinkled with toasted sliced almonds.

M2/Life Modification: Add 1 medium peeled and diced Idaho potato to the pot with the broth.

Creamy Cauliflower Soup with Bacon

The flavor of smoky bacon highlights this rich and satisfying soup.

1 Tbsp. olive oil

1 large leek, white part only, roughly chopped

1 medium head cauliflower, trimmed and roughly chopped

5 cups Basic Chicken or Vegetable Broth (see page 21 or 22)

6 to 8 drops Capella Sizzlin' Bacon

Salt and pepper to taste

¼ cup unsweetened almond milk

Dash paprika

2 bacon slices, cooked crisp, drained, and crumbled

1. Heat oil over medium heat in a soup pot. Add the leek and cook over medium-low heat until softened but not browned, stirring often, about 4 minutes.
2. Stir in cauliflower and broth, increase heat to high, and bring to a boil. Add the Capella, reduce heat to medium-low, and simmer, stirring occasionally, until cauliflower is fork tender, about 20 minutes.
3. Working in batches, puree soup in a blender. Return to pot, add almond milk if using, and taste for the addition of salt and pepper. Serve piping hot with a dash of paprika and a sprinkle of bacon bits.

Makes 4 servings (125 calories; 4.5 grams protein, 5 grams fat, 11 grams carbohydrates)

M1 Caution Modification: Substitute real bacon bits for the Capella Sizzlin' Bacon.

M2/Life Modification: Add 1 cup cubed potatoes in Step 2 and top with shredded cheddar cheese upon serving.

Napa Sunshine Slaw

Light and refreshing, you'll love this slaw with its hint of dill and the tang of orange zest.

4 cups (about 1 lb.) Napa (Chinese) cabbage, thinly sliced
1 large carrot, peeled and coarsely grated
1 Tbsp. fresh dill, chopped
3 Tbsp. olive oil
1 Tbsp. white wine vinegar

Salt and pepper to taste
½ tsp. grated orange zest
8 to 10 drops Sweetleaf Stevia Valencia Orange
2 Clementine or Mandarin oranges, peeled and segmented

1. In a medium bowl, toss together cabbage, carrot, and dill.
2. In a small bowl, whisk together remaining ingredients except for the orange segments. Pour over cabbage mixture and toss well to coat.
3. Stir in orange segments and set aside at room temperature for 15 minutes. Taste for seasoning before serving.

Makes 6 servings (100 calories; 7 grams fat, 1 gram protein, 7 grams carbohydrates)

M1 Caution Modification: Stir in ¼ cup shelled sunflower seeds.

M2/Life Modification: Stir in ½ cup sour cream and chill well before serving.

Spring Green Salad with Prosciutto and Fig

Tender spring greens get a sweet dressing of balsamic vinegar and fig in this terrific salad that's great for lunch.

2 cups spring greens, washed and patted or spun dry
2 Tbsp. prosciutto, diced (Caution)
1 Tbsp. dried fig, diced
½ small red onion, thinly sliced

1 Tbsp. olive oil
2 tsp. balsamic vinegar
6 drops Capella Fig
8 drops Clear Stevia
Salt and pepper to taste

1. In a medium bowl, toss together the greens, prosciutto, fig, and red onion. In a small bowl, whisk together the remaining ingredients and pour over the salad mixture.
2. Toss gently to coat, taste for the addition of salt and pepper, transfer to a large plate, and serve immediately.

Makes 1 serving (260 calories; 11 grams protein, 18 grams fat, 15 grams carbohydrates)

Primavera Salad

Crunchy vegetables form the base of this healthy salad that's perfect for upgrading to a low-carb pasta salad.

1 cup broccoli florets, cooked to crisp tender

1 cup green beans, cooked to crisp tender

½ medium red bell pepper, seeded and thinly sliced

½ cup carrots, shredded

½ medium red onion, cut into thin circles

1 cup grape tomatoes, halved

¼ cup extra virgin olive oil

2 Tbsp. balsamic vinegar

8 drops Sweetleaf Stevia Grape

1 tsp. prepared mustard

1 small garlic clove, minced

1 Tbsp. finely chopped fresh basil

Salt and pepper to taste

1. In a large bowl, combine the broccoli, green beans, bell pepper, carrots, red onion, and tomatoes.
2. In a small bowl, whisk together olive oil, vinegar, Stevia, mustard, and garlic. Pour over the vegetable mixture and toss well to coat. Stir in chopped basil and season with salt and pepper. Serve at room temperature.

Makes 6 servings (43 calories; 9 grams fat, 1 gram protein, 8 grams carbohydrates)

M1 Caution Modification: Add 1 cup diced mozzarella cheese cubes.

M2/Life Modification: Stir in 2 cups cooked whole grain pasta such as penne.

Sesame Peanut Salad

This version of a popular Chinese preparation gets a boost of flavor from the unique tastes of Capella.

3 green onions, thinly sliced
½ yellow or orange bell pepper, seeded and thinly sliced
⅔ cup fresh snow peas, thinly sliced
½ cup carrots, shredded
2 cups fresh bean sprouts

2 tsp. coconut oil
⅓ cup Bragg Liquid Amino
2 Tbsp. unsweetened rice vinegar
6 drops Capella Peanut Butter
5 drops Capella Coconut
¼ tsp. Clear Stevia
Salt and pepper to taste

1. In a large bowl, toss together the green onions, bell pepper, snow peas, carrots, and bean sprouts.
2. In a small bowl, whisk together the oil, liquid aminos, vinegar, Capella, and Stevia. Pour over the vegetable mixture and toss well to coat. Season with salt and pepper and chill for one hour before serving.

Makes 4 servings (100 calories; 7 grams fat, 1 gram protein, 8 grams carbohydrates)

M1 Caution Modification: Replace the coconut oil with sesame oil and whisk ¼ cup peanut butter into the dressing before pouring over the vegetables.

M2/Life Modification: Add 4 oz. Chinese egg noodles, cooked according to package directions, and a sprinkling of chopped peanuts.

Caesar's Grilled Green Goddess Salad

Creamy avocado is the base for the delicious dressing that replaces the usual Caesar recipe. Use this on other salads and as a topping for grilled chicken and seafood.

For the Dressing:

1 avocado, peeled, seeded, and diced
1 Tbsp. lemon juice
8 to 10 drops Sweetleaf Stevia Lemon Drop
2 Tbsp. unsweetened plain almond milk

¼ cup olive oil
2 Tbsp. fresh parsley
½ tsp. prepared mustard
Salt and pepper to taste

For the Salad:

2 Romaine lettuce hearts
Olive oil for brushing

Salt and pepper to taste

1. Make the dressing by combining all the ingredients in a blender and pureeing until smooth. Transfer to an airtight container and keep refrigerated.
2. Slice the romaine hearts in half the long way and carefully trim the core ends without allowing the leaves to detach.
3. Have ready a grill on medium heat. Lightly brush the cut sides of the romaine hearts with a little oil and season with salt and pepper, if using. Grill the hearts cut side down, just until grill marks are visible and the cut leaves have slightly warmed and wilted.
4. Transfer to serving plates and drizzle the dressing on top. Serve immediately.

Makes 4 servings (206 calories; 21 grams fat, 4 grams protein, 2 grams carbohydrates)

M1 Caution Modification: Replace the almond milk with light or regular mayonnaise.

M2/Life Modification: Sprinkle with a little crumbled bacon and shredded Parmesan cheese before serving.

Salmon Salad Niçoise

Salmon replaces the usual canned tuna in this main course salad that's super satisfying and adaptable to additional ingredients.

For the Salad:

3 cups dark leafy salad greens

1 cup fresh green beans, cooked and chilled

2 medium-sized ripe tomatoes, cut into wedges

2 Tbsp. Niçoise olives, drained

½ medium green bell pepper, seeded and cut into ¼-inch-thick rings

½ cup cucumber, sliced

1 cup broccoli florets, cooked to crisp tender

For the Dressing:

Juice of 1 lemon

5 drops Sweetleaf Stevia Valencia Orange

5 drops Sweetleaf Stevia Lemon Drop

2 Tbsp. olive oil

Salt and pepper to taste

2 tsp. fresh dill, chopped

6 oz. boneless salmon filet, poached or baked

1 egg, hard boiled, peeled, and quartered

1. In a large mixing bowl, gently toss together lettuce, green beans, tomatoes, olives, bell pepper, cucumber, and broccoli. In a small bowl, whisk together the lemon juice, Stevia, oil, salt, pepper, and dill. Pour over the salad greens, toss gently, and set aside for 15 minutes.
2. Break the salmon into bite-sized pieces and gently fold into the salad. Divide between 2 plates and top with the egg. Serve immediately.

Makes 2 servings. (380 calories; 30 grams fat, 23 grams protein, 13 grams carbohydrates)

M1 Caution Modification: Increase olive oil by 1 Tbsp. and add 1 cup baby arugula to the greens.

M2/Life Modification: Add 1 medium red potato, boiled and sliced, to the vegetable mixture.

DRESSINGS, SAUCES, AND CONDIMENTS

MAINTENANCE

ALTHOUGH THE OPTIONS for choosing accompanying dressings and sauces are greater during the Maintenance phase, many of the prepackaged selections have preservatives, sweeteners, and unwanted sugar or starch. Here you'll find some versatile recipes for common accompaniments that will enhance your eating pleasure during this time and provide the taste you are after without the doubt or worry of processed foods.

As with all Maintenance recipes, monitor both your "Caution" selections and calorie counts as you progress each week. Be sure to only introduce your allotted sugars and starches when allowed. Although the calorie counts given are as accurate as possible, please consult the nutritional labels of the specific products used to be sure.

Cucumber Raita with Crudités
(Recipe on page 191)

House Italian Dressing

Bold garlic and herbs are featured in this easy and flavorful dressing alternative to commercial brands that may contain sugar or additives.

1 large garlic clove, minced	4 drops Sweetleaf Stevia Lemon Drop
1 tsp. prepared mustard	3 drops Clear Stevia
1 Tbsp. Italian dried herb blend	⅔ cup olive oil
⅓ cup white or red wine vinegar	Salt and pepper to taste

1. In a medium mixing bowl, whisk together the garlic, mustard, herb blend, vinegar, and Stevia.
2. Slowly add the olive oil while whisking until dressing is thick and satiny. Season to taste with salt and pepper. Keep refrigerated for up to 1 week.

Makes 16 servings. (80 calories; 144 grams fat)

M1 Caution Modification: Whisk in 2 Tbsp. grated Parmesan or Romano cheese.

M2/Life Modification: Replace half the olive oil with ⅓ cup plain low-fat yogurt, sour cream, or soft tofu for a creamy Italian version.

Cucumber Raita with Crudités

A wonderfully cooling accompaniment for spicy dishes such as curries, this tasty sauce is also great with grilled meats, chicken, and fish, as well as a dip for raw vegetables.

1½ cups whipped cottage cheese	3 or 4 drops Capella Cool Mint
2 Tbsp. unsweetened plain almond milk	6 drops Clear Stevia
	1 Tbsp. chopped fresh mint
1 cup cucumber, diced	1 Tbsp. chopped fresh coriander
1 tsp. lime juice	Salt and pepper to taste

1. Whisk together the cottage cheese and almond milk in a medium bowl. Stir in the remaining ingredients, tasting for the addition of salt and/or Stevia.
2. Refrigerate for at least 1 hour before serving. Keep refrigerated for up to 3 days.

Makes 6 servings (50 calories; 1.5 grams fat, 7 grams protein, 2 grams carbohydrates)

M1 Caution Modification: Replace the cottage cheese with nonfat Greek yogurt.

M2/Life Modification: Eliminate the Clear Stevia and stir in 1 tsp. honey.

Quick Tartar Sauce

This homemade stand-in for bottled versions features fresh aromatic herbs and the wonderfully piquant flavor of pickles and capers.

1 cup cottage cheese

Juice of ½ a lemon

4 drops Sweetleaf Stevia Valencia Orange

5 drops Clear Stevia

1 Tbsp. capers, drained and chopped

2 Tbsp. dill pickle, chopped

2 tsp. fresh parsley, finely chopped

1 tsp. fresh tarragon, finely chopped

Dash Frank's Hot Sauce

Salt to taste

1. In a blender, combine the cottage cheese, lemon juice, Stevia, capers, pickles, parsley, tarragon, and hot sauce and puree until smooth.
2. Transfer to an airtight container and taste for the addition of salt. Refrigerate for at least 1 hour before using. Keep refrigerated for up to 3 days.

Makes 8 servings (25 calories; 1 gram fat, 4 grams protein, 1 gram carbohydrates)

M1 Caution Modification: Replace half the cottage cheese with light or regular mayonnaise or plain Greek yogurt.

M2/Life Modification: Replace all the cottage cheese with light or regular mayonnaise.

Homemade Marinara Sauce

Bottled spaghetti sauce can move over when this delicious version is on the menu, handy for everything from saucing up vegetables to spooning over pasta in M2/Life phases.

2 Tbsp. olive oil	2 cups water
1 medium onion, diced	8 to 10 drops Sweetleaf Stevia Grape
Salt and pepper to taste	
2 garlic cloves, minced	1 Tbsp. dried parsley
28-oz. can crushed plum tomatoes, no sugar	1 Tbsp. dried oregano
	1 Tbsp. dried basil
2 Tbsp. tomato paste	1 bay leaf

1. In a large heavy-bottomed pot, heat the olive oil over medium heat. Add the onion, season with salt and pepper, and cook, stirring until softened, about 5 minutes. Add the garlic and cook another minute.
2. Stir in the remaining ingredients and bring to a simmer. Cook at a very low boil, uncovered, until thickened and reduced, about 1 hour. Taste for additional seasoning and serve immediately or store for future use.

Makes 8 servings (60 calories; 4 grams fat, 1 gram protein, 5 grams carbohydrates)

M1 Caution Modification: Stir in 2 Tbsp. grated Parmesan or Romano cheese 5 minutes before serving.

M2/Life Modification: Add ¼ cup dry red wine when adding the tomatoes.

Romesco Sauce

Smoky and flavorful, this classic Spanish sauce is all you need for everything from grilling vegetables to roasting fish and poultry.

1 large red bell pepper
3 medium tomatoes
2 garlic cloves, minced
1 tsp. chili powder
1 tsp. paprika
1 Tbsp. fresh parsley, chopped

2 Tbsp. sherry vinegar
4 drops Sweetleaf Stevia Hazelnut
3 drops Capella Amaretto
¼ cup olive oil
Salt and pepper to taste

1. Under a broiler or over an open flame, char the bell pepper. Set in a paper bag to cool slightly and remove the blackened skin by scraping. Cut in half, core, and roughly chop.
2. Cut the tomatoes in half and char the skin sides just briefly under the broiler to remove. Cut out the cores and roughly chop.
3. Place the chopped pepper, tomatoes, and all the remaining ingredients in a food processor and puree until smooth. Transfer to a container and taste for seasoning. Refrigerate until ready to serve.

Makes 6 servings (110 calories; 9 grams fat, 6 grams carbohydrates)

M1 Caution Modification: Add 2 Tbsp. chopped almonds and/or hazelnuts to the processor.

M2/Life Modification: Add a 2-inch slice of toasted Italian bread, roughly cut, to the food processor.

Sweet and Spicy Sauce

This versatile sauce is great to have on hand for all types of burgers as well as grilled chicken and kebabs.

¼ cup Worcestershire sauce
½ cup tomato paste
1 cup water
Juice of ½ an orange
10 drops Sweetleaf Stevia Valencia Orange

1 tsp. minced ginger
1 garlic clove, minced
¼ tsp. cayenne pepper, or more to taste
Salt to taste

1. Combine all the ingredients in a medium saucepan and bring to a boil over medium-high heat, stirring often. Reduce heat to low, and allow to simmer until thickened and reduced by half, 12 to 15 minutes, stirring often to prevent sticking.
2. Transfer to a container and chill for at least 2 hours. Taste for additional seasoning before serving.

Makes 8 servings (20 calories; 6 grams carbohydrates)

M1 Caution Modification: Replace the orange juice with ¼ cup mango juice.

M2/Life Modification: Add 1 Tbsp. minced golden raisins when cooking.

POULTRY ENTRÉES

DELICIOUS IDEAS FOR chicken, turkey, and other poultry selections are featured here, all using the fabulous flavors of Capella and Stevia. From exotic spiced chicken breasts to classic dishes like duck with orange sauce, you'll be hard pressed to decide which recipe to make next!

When chicken broth is called for, feel free to use the broth recipe included in the VLCD soup section on page 21, or you may use a store-bought version as well, provided it is low in sodium and carbs and has zero sugars.

As with all Maintenance recipes, monitor both your "Caution" selections and calorie counts as you progress each week. Be sure to only introduce your allotted sugars and starches when allowed. Although the calorie counts given are as accurate as possible, please consult the nutritional labels of the specific products used to be sure.

Cornish Hens with Apricot Stuffing
(Recipe on page 206)

Super Juicy Roast Lemon Chicken

Tangy lemon and flavorful onion help to seal in moisture in this delicious, rosemary-scented entrée of roasted chicken quarters.

4 chicken leg quarters
2 lemons, cut into ¼-inch slices
4 rosemary sprigs
1 small onion, thinly sliced
1 Tbsp. olive oil

Salt and pepper to taste
½ cup water
10 drops Sweetleaf Stevia Lemon Drop

1. Preheat the oven to 400° F.
2. Place the lemon slices in a single layer, close to each other, in the bottom of a roasting pan. Place the rosemary sprigs on top.
3. Tuck the onion slices under the skin of each chicken quarter by carefully loosening the skin from the meat with your fingertips. Rub each quarter with olive oil and season with salt and pepper.
4. Place each quarter on top of the lemons and rosemary. Combine the water and Stevia and pour around the edge of the pan. Roast in the oven until the skin is golden and an internal read thermometer registers 175° F in the thighs, 40 to 50 minutes, basting occasionally with the accumulated pan juices.
5. Remove from the oven and allow to rest for 10 minutes before transferring the chicken to a heated serving platter and topping each with some of the cooked lemon slices and pan juice. Remove skin before eating, if desired.

Makes 4 servings (With skin: 430 calories; 31 grams fat, 34 grams protein)

M1 Caution Modification: Roast 1½ cups butternut squash chunks with the chicken.

M2/Life Modification: Roast 12 baby potatoes with the chicken.

Roasted Spiced Chicken Breasts

Exotically spiced and deliciously accompanied by roasted dried plums, this Middle Eastern dish will quickly become a dinner favorite.

2 split chicken breasts on the bone, skin removed	Salt and pepper to taste
2 Tbsp. olive oil	8 dried plums (prunes)
½ tsp. ground cumin	Juice of 1 orange
½ tsp. ground cinnamon	8 drops Sweetleaf Stevia
¼ tsp. ground cardamom	Cinnamon
	Lemon wedges for serving

1. Preheat the oven to 425° F.
2. In a small bowl, whisk together olive oil, cumin, cinnamon, and cardamom. Season the chicken with salt and pepper and place skin-side up in a medium roasting pan. Drizzle oil mixture over top and roast chicken for 15 minutes.
3. Meanwhile, combine the prunes, orange juice, and Stevia in a bowl and soak for at least 10 minutes. After the chicken has roasted for 15 minutes, add the prune mixture to the roasting pan, stir, and continue to cook until the chicken reaches an internal temperature of 165° F or is golden and firm to the touch, about 20 minutes more.
4. Remove from the oven and allow to rest for 10 minutes before serving with the lemon wedges.

Makes 2 servings (350 calories; 15 grams fat, 14 grams protein, 28 grams carbohydrates)

M1 Caution Modification: Add ½ cup canned, drained chickpeas when adding the prunes.

M2/Life Modification: Add 1 medium peeled and diced sweet potato to roasting pan in Step 2.

Curry Chicken Kebabs

Aromatic skewers of tender and flavorful chicken and vegetables fit the bill for grill night during Maintenance and are easily upgraded with tasty embellishments.

6 boneless skinless chicken thighs
1 Tbsp. curry powder
Juice of 1 lemon
¼ tsp. Clear Stevia
1 large green bell pepper, seeded and cut into chunks
1 large red onion, peeled and cut into chunks

½ cup Chicken Broth (see page 21)
1 tsp. Worcestershire sauce
12 or 15 drops Sweetleaf Stevia Apricot Nectar
2 tsp. vegetable oil
Salt and pepper to taste
Metal skewers for grilling

1. In a shallow bowl, stir together curry powder, lemon juice, and Clear Stevia until smooth. Cut chicken thighs into bite-sized pieces and marinate in the curry mixture for 20 minutes.
2. Meanwhile, place broth, Worcestershire sauce, and Stevia in a small saucepan and cook over medium-low heat for about 3 minutes. Set aside and keep warm.
4. Heat an outdoor or indoor grill to medium-high and coat lightly with oil. Thread skewers with chicken, bell pepper, and onion, and season with salt and pepper. Grill kebabs on all sides until browned and chicken juices run clear, about 12 minutes.
5. To serve, transfer to a platter and cover with sauce.

Makes 4 servings (173 calories; 10 grams fat, 13 grams protein, 6 grams carbohydrates)

M1 Caution Modification: Serve with a dollop of Cucumber Raita (see page 191).

M2/Life Modification: Serve on a bed of brown basmati rice.

Quick Pan-Fried Chicken and Gravy

Ready in minutes, you'll definitely love this version of a Southern favorite served up with a creamy, delicious white gravy. Count as a Caution selection.

1 lb. chicken breast cutlets, sliced thin
Salt and pepper to taste
⅔ cup almond flour
1 tsp. paprika
3 Tbsp. coconut or light olive oil
⅔ cup Chicken Broth (see page 21)
⅓ cup unsweetened almond milk
6 drops Sweetleaf Stevia Vanilla Crème

1. Season the chicken cutlets with salt and pepper. In a shallow bowl, stir together all but 2 tablespoons of the flour with the paprika.
2. Heat the oil in a large nonstick skillet over medium-high heat. Generously dredge the cutlets in the flour mixture and fry in the hot oil until golden brown, about 4 minutes per side. Transfer to paper towels to drain and pour off all but 2 tablespoons of the remaining oil.
3. Whisk in the reserved 2 tablespoons of flour to form a paste, cooking over medium heat. Slowly add the chicken broth, whisking constantly, to prevent lumps. Add the almond milk and Stevia and cook over low, stirring constantly until thickened, about 2 minutes more.
4. Place the cooked cutlets on serving plates. Taste the gravy for seasoning and serve immediately spooned over the chicken.

Makes 4 servings (320 calories; 18 grams fat, 27 grams protein, 2 grams carbohydrates)

M1 Caution Modification: Replace almond milk with half & half.

M2/Life Modification: Replace almond flour with all-purpose flour.

Kicked Up Chicken Burgers

A super flavorful departure from typical burgers, smoke and spice turn this casual dinner fare into a fiesta.

1 lb. ground chicken or turkey
1 Tbsp. coconut or olive oil
½ medium onion, finely chopped
½ medium red bell pepper, finely chopped
1 small celery stalk, finely diced
1 small carrot, finely diced
½ cup mushrooms, roughly chopped

1 Tbsp. dried cranberries, no sugar added
8 drops Sweetleaf Stevia Berry
Salt and pepper to taste
1 garlic clove, minced
1 large egg white
2 Tbsp. ground flax seeds

1. Heat oil in a medium skillet over medium heat. Add onion, red bell pepper, celery, carrot, mushrooms, cranberries, Stevia, salt, and pepper and cook, stirring often, until soft but not browned, about 5 minutes. Add garlic and cook another minute. Set aside to cool.
2. Preheat an outdoor grill to medium-high and brush lightly with oil.
3. In a large bowl, combine cooked vegetables, ground chicken, egg white, and ground flaxseeds. Mix well with a fork or your hands and shape into 4 burgers.
4. Grill until burgers are cooked through and nicely browned, about 6 minutes per side. Serve immediately.

Makes 4 servings (255 calories; 14 grams fat, 22 grams protein, 11 grams carbohydrates)

M1 Caution Modification: Turn into a cheeseburger with a slice of your favorite cheese.

M2/Life Modification: Serve on a low-carb or light hamburger bun.

Chicken Tenders with Mushroom Sauce

Tender is definitely the word for these delicious morsels lightly sautéed with a hint of garlic and topped with a creamy mushroom sauce.

1 lb. chicken tenderloins, white tendon removed
Salt and pepper to taste
2 Tbsp. coconut or olive oil
10 oz. white mushrooms, trimmed and thinly sliced
2 garlic cloves, minced
¼ cup water
8 drops Sweetleaf Stevia Grape
½ cup chicken broth
¼ cup unsweetened plain almond milk

1. Season the tenderloins with salt and pepper and set aside.
2. Heat the oil in a large nonstick skillet over medium heat. Lightly brown the chicken tenders, about 2 minutes per side, and transfer to a clean plate.
3. Add the mushrooms to the pan and cook over medium heat, stirring occasionally, until lightly browned, about 6 minutes. Stir in the garlic and cook another 2 minutes.
4. Add the water and Stevia and stir until the liquid has evaporated, then add the broth and bring to a simmer.
5. Return the chicken to the skillet, reduce the heat to low, then cover and simmer until cooked through, about 4 minutes. Transfer the chicken to a heated serving platter and add the almond milk to the skillet.
6. Cook the mushroom sauce, stirring often, until bubbly and thickened, about 2 minutes. Taste for seasoning, spoon over the chicken tenders, and serve immediately.

Makes 4 servings (210 calories; 8 grams fat, 28 grams protein, 3 grams carbohydrates)

M1 Caution Modification: Replace half the oil with butter and/or the almond milk with light cream.

M2/Life Modification: Replace the water with dry white wine.

Chicken Vegetable Korma

Almonds, ginger, and garlic combine to create great flavor in this delicious version of an Indian classic.

2 boneless, skinless chicken breasts, cut into bite-sized pieces
1 Tbsp. fresh ginger, roughly chopped
3 garlic cloves, roughly chopped
½ cup unsweetened almond milk
4 drops Capella Amaretto
8 drops Clear Stevia
1 Tbsp. coconut or olive oil
Salt and pepper to taste

1 medium onion, diced
1 medium red bell pepper, cored and diced
1 medium carrot, peeled and sliced
1 cinnamon stick
1 bay leaf
1 tsp. mild curry powder
1 cup chicken broth or water

1. Combine the ginger, garlic, almond milk, Capella, and Stevia in a food processor or blender and puree until contents create a smooth almond paste. Set aside.
2. Heat the oil in a large nonstick skillet over medium heat. Add the chicken pieces, season with salt and pepper, and cook until no longer pink, but not cooked through, about 4 minutes. Transfer to a clean bowl with a slotted spoon and set aside.
3. Add the onion, bell pepper, and carrot to the skillet and cook over medium heat, stirring often, until softened, about 5 minutes. Stir in the cinnamon stick, bay leaf, and curry powder and continue to cook for 1 minute more.
4. Stir in the blended almond paste and broth, return the chicken to the skillet with its accumulated juices, and bring to a low simmer. Cover, reduce the heat to low, and cook until the chicken is no longer pink inside and the vegetables are tender, about 12 minutes. Remove the lid and allow sauce to thicken slightly, if necessary, cooking on low for 2 minutes and stirring occasionally.
5. Taste the sauce for seasoning, remove the cinnamon stick and bay leaf, and transfer to a bowl for serving.

Makes 2 servings (325 calories; 15 grams fat, 15 grams protein, 12 grams carbohydrates)

M1 Caution Modification: Add ¼ cup slivered almonds to the almond milk mixture before blending.

M2/Life Modification: Add 1 small peeled and diced sweet potato with the vegetables and/or serve over basmati rice.

Cornish Hens with Apricot Stuffing

Delicious little game hens are perfect for quickly stuffing and here apricots take center stage for a sweet and fruity accompaniment.

For the Stuffing:

1 Tbsp. coconut or olive oil
¼ cup onion, finely chopped
½ cup celery, chopped
1 cup fresh or canned (no sugar added) apricots, diced

1 small Red Delicious apple, cored and diced
¼ tsp. dried thyme
2 tsp. fresh parsley, finely chopped
Salt and pepper to taste

For the Cornish Hens:

2 Cornish game hens, giblets and fat removed, rinsed and patted dry
2 tsp. vegetable oil
½ cup water

6 drops Sweetleaf Stevia Apricot Nectar
3 drops Capella Apple Pie
6 drops Clear Stevia

1. Preheat the oven to 400° F.
2. Heat the oil in a skillet over medium heat, add onion and celery, and cook, stirring often, until softened, about 3 minutes. Add apricots, apple, thyme, parsley, salt, and pepper and continue to cook, stirring often, until apple is fork tender, 5 to 7 minutes. Transfer to a medium bowl to cool slightly.
3. Combine the water, Capella, and Stevia in a small cup. Fill cavities of hens with stuffing and place on a rack in a roasting pan. Coat skin with oil, season with salt and pepper, and pour flavored water in bottom of pan.
4. Roast hens, basting every 15 minutes with pan juices, until skin is crisp and golden and juices run clear when thigh is pierced with a fork, about 1 hour, 10 minutes total.
5. Transfer hens to a platter, let rest for 10 minutes, and serve with pan juices.

Makes 4 servings (460 calories; 34 grams fat, 29 grams protein, 8 grams carbohydrates)

M1 Caution Modification: Add ½ cup roughly chopped chestnuts to the stuffing.

M2/Life Modification: Add 1 medium corn muffin, crumbled, and ¼ cup chicken broth to the stuffing.

Turkey Picadillo

A Latin American favorite, this flavorful stew can also be made with leftover roasted chicken or duck.

1 Tbsp. olive oil
1 medium onion, chopped
Salt and pepper to taste
2 garlic cloves, minced
1½ cups turkey breast, cooked and roughly chopped
½ cup pitted green olives, roughly chopped

Juice of 1 orange
½ cup chicken broth
6 drops Sweetleaf Stevia Valencia Orange
1½ cups low-sodium canned diced tomatoes, with liquid
1 bay leaf

1. Heat the oil in a stewing pot over medium heat. Add the onion, season with salt and pepper, and cook, stirring occasionally, until soft but not browned, about 4 minutes. Add the garlic and cook another minute.
2. Stir in the turkey, olives, broth, orange juice, Stevia, tomatoes with their liquid, and bay leaf and bring to a simmer. Reduce the heat to low and simmer for 12 minutes, stirring occasionally.
3. Taste for seasoning and serve immediately.

Makes 2 servings (305 calories; 14 grams fat, 34 grams protein, 25 grams carbohydrates)

M1 Caution Modification: Add 2 Tbsp. golden raisins during the last 5 minutes of simmering.

M2/Life Modification: Serve over plain couscous or rice.

Turkey and Eggplant Chili

This flavorful version of an old favorite gets added interest from carrots and eggplant, with the addition of beans allowed as a tasty upgrade.

1 Tbsp. olive oil

1 medium onion, peeled and diced

1 medium green bell pepper, seeded and diced

2 medium carrots, peeled and diced

Salt and pepper to taste

1 medium eggplant, ends trimmed, peeled, and cut into ½-inch cubes

1 lb. ground turkey or chicken

1 cup low-sodium tomato sauce

1½ cups low-sodium canned diced tomatoes, with their juices

1 cup water

6 drops Sweetleaf Stevia Grape

3 drops Sweetleaf Stevia Chocolate

3 Tbsp. chili powder

1 Tbsp. paprika

1 tsp. ground cumin

⅛ tsp. cayenne pepper, or more to taste

1. Heat the oil in a medium-sized heavy-bottomed pot over medium heat, add the onion, bell pepper, and carrot, season with salt and pepper, and cook until somewhat softened, stirring a few times, about 8 minutes.
2. Add the eggplant and a touch more oil and continue to cook, stirring often, until the eggplant has softened a bit, about 5 minutes. Add the ground turkey and, using a fork, break up any clumps that form, cooking just until no longer pink.
3. Stir in the tomato sauce, tomatoes with their juices, water, Stevia, and spices and bring to a simmer. Reduce the heat to low, cover, and cook, stirring occasionally, until the vegetables are tender and the sauce has thickened, about 15 minutes. Taste for seasoning and serve immediately.

Makes 4 servings (295 calories; 13 grams fat, 24 grams protein, 23 grams carbohydrates)

M1 Caution Modification: Stir in 1 cup kidney or black beans 5 minutes before serving.

M2/Life Modification: Serve over rice or noodles with a sprinkling of grated cheddar cheese or a dollop of sour cream.

Holiday Spiced Turkey Breast with Cranberries

This super delicious entrée will have others at the table glaring with envy when you dig in and savor the festive flavors.

¼ cup fresh cranberries, roughly chopped
Juice of 1 orange
4 to 6 drops Capella Pumpkin Pie Spice
15 drops Clear Stevia

1 Tbsp. olive oil
Salt and pepper to taste
4 boneless turkey breast cutlets
¼ cup chicken or vegetable broth
2 tsp. fresh parsley, chopped

1. In a small bowl, combine the cranberries, orange juice, Capella, and Stevia and set aside for 15 minutes.
2. Heat the oil over medium-high heat in a large nonstick skillet and season the turkey cutlets with salt and pepper. Brown the cutlets evenly on both sides and transfer to a clean plate.
3. Add the broth to the skillet and scrape up any residue over high heat. Add the cranberry mixture, reduce the heat to medium low, and return the turkey cutlets (along with any accumulated juices) to the skillet. Stir and cook, covered, until the turkey is done, 6 to 8 minutes and the sauce has thickened.
4. Transfer to a serving platter and spoon the cranberry sauce mixture over the cutlets. Garnish with the parsley and serve immediately.

Makes 2 servings (290 calories; 41 grams protein, 9 grams fat, 9 grams carbohydrates)

M1 Caution Modification: Add 1 cup cooked and cubed butternut squash to the skillet to warm through just before serving.

M2/Life Modification: Add 1 cup cooked and cubed pumpkin or sweet potato to the skillet to warm through just before serving and/or swirl in a pat of unsalted butter.

Seared Duck Breast with Orange Sauce

Here's a gourmet treat that's sure to delight, devoid of all the usual sugar in the classic version thanks to Stevia.

2 large boneless duck breasts
Salt and pepper to taste

For the Orange Sauce:

1 tsp. light olive oil
1 medium shallot, peeled and
    finely chopped
Juice of 2 oranges
½ cup chicken broth
2 Tbsp. sherry vinegar

15 drops Sweetleaf Stevia
    Valencia Orange
8 drops Clear Stevia
¼ tsp. orange zest
½ cup Mandarin orange
    segments, roughly chopped

1. To make the orange sauce, begin by heating the oil in a medium saucepan over medium heat. Then, cook the shallot until softened, 3 to 4 minutes. Add the orange juice, broth, vinegar, Stevia, and zest and whisk well to combine. Increase the heat to medium-high and allow to boil and reduce by half, about 10 minutes. Set aside.
2. Preheat the oven to 450° F. Using a sharp paring knife, score the duck breast skins, making a crosshatch pattern, being careful not to cut into the meat. Sprinkle both sides with salt and pepper.
3. Heat a large, heavy-bottomed skillet over high heat and place the duck breasts skin-side down. Fry until the skin is brown and crisp, about 8 minutes, then turn over and cook for an additional 2 minutes. Transfer the duck to a medium roasting pan and finish cooking in the oven to the desired degree of doneness, about 20 minutes for medium-rare. Allow to rest out of the oven for 5 to 8 minutes before slicing.
4. Finish the sauce by bringing it back to a boil and stirring in the orange segments. Taste for seasoning and additional Stevia and spoon over the sliced duck breasts. Serve immediately.

Makes 4 servings (300 calories; 10 grams fat, 29 grams protein, 6 grams carbohydrates)

M1 Caution Modification: Swirl 1 Tbsp. of unsalted butter into the sauce before serving.

M2/Life Modification: Serve with wild rice or brown rice pilaf.

MEATY ENTRÉES

FROM BEEF AND VEAL to pork and lamb, you'll find some mighty meaty entrée choices in this section that make great use of the expanded list of allowed ingredients as well as the super flavors of Capella and Stevia. Many of the dishes are meals in themselves or can be combined with the salads or side dishes in the Maintenance phase.

When beef broth is called for, feel free to use the broth recipe included in the VLCD soup section, or you may use a purchased version as well, provided it is low in sodium, carbs, and zero sugars.

As with all Maintenance recipes, monitor both your "Caution" selections and calorie counts as you progress each week. Be sure to only introduce your allotted sugars and starches when allowed. Although the calorie counts given are as accurate as possible, please consult the nutritional labels of the specific products used to be sure.

Loin Lamb Chops with Apricot Mustard Glaze
(Recipe on page 224)

The Best Beef Brisket

You can just as easily make this in a slow cooker according to manufacturer's directions, but the wait will be longer!

3-lb. beef brisket, trimmed of fat
1 Tbsp. olive oil
2 garlic cloves, minced
1 tsp. dried thyme
Salt and pepper to taste

2 large onions, halved and sliced
28-oz. can of plum tomatoes with juices, roughly chopped
½ cup beef broth
1 serving of Clear Crisp Cola (see page 3)

1. Preheat the oven to 325° F.
2. Place the brisket in a roasting pan or Dutch oven. Rub the garlic and thyme over the meat and sprinkle with salt and pepper. Cover with the onions and tomatoes and pour the broth and cola around the pan.
3. Cover with foil or a lid and cook until tender, occasionally turning the brisket and stirring the sauce, about 3 to 4 hours.
4. When fork tender, transfer the brisket to a platter. Pour the liquid mixture into a large saucepan and simmer to thicken, if necessary. Taste for seasoning and serve with the sliced brisket.

Makes about 6 servings (270 calories; 19 grams fat, 15 grams protein, 9 grams carbohydrates)

M1 Caution Modification: Add ½ cup carrot juice to the roasting pan.

M1/Life Modification: Serve with ½ cup mashed potatoes.

Teriyaki Beef with Snow Peas

Thin slices of beef take on abundant flavor when marinated before cooking in this easy stir-fry recipe full of delicious and healthy Asian vegetables.

For the Marinade:

½ cup low-sodium soy sauce or Bragg Liquid Aminos

1 Tbsp. plain rice vinegar

8 drops Sweetleaf Stevia Lemon Drop

⅛ tsp. Clear Stevia

2 tsp. minced fresh ginger

1 large garlic clove, minced

For the Beef:

8 oz. beef tenderloin or sirloin, sliced into thin strips

1 Tbsp. coconut or olive oil

1 bunch scallions, ends trimmed and cut into 1½-inch pieces

½ cup carrots, shredded

Salt and pepper to taste

1 cup fresh snow peas

¼ tsp. sesame seeds

1. In a medium glass baking dish, combine the marinade ingredients and stir well with a fork. Add the beef slices and allow to marinate for at least 30 minutes, turning them over halfway through.
2. Heat the oil in a wok or large nonstick skillet over high heat. Remove the beef from the marinade and lightly pat dry with a paper towel. Fry it in the oil (do not stir-fry or move around in the pan) until the edges are golden and crisp, about 3 minutes per side. Transfer to the middle of a large heated platter.
3. Add a touch more oil to the wok or skillet and heat to nearly smoking. Add the scallions and carrots, sprinkle with salt and pepper, and stir-fry over high heat for 2 minutes. Add the snow peas, season again with salt and pepper, and continue to stir-fry another minute. Add the sesame seeds and transfer the vegetables to the outside of the platter, surrounding the beef, and serve immediately.

Makes 2 servings (350 calories; 23 grams fat, 27 grams protein, 14 grams carbohydrates)

M1 Caution Modification: Add 1 cup mung or soy bean sprouts with the snow peas and/or drizzle a little sesame oil over all before serving.

M2/Life Modification: Serve with ½ cup cooked Asian noodles or rice per serving.

Hearty Beef Stroganoff

A delicious and creamy sauce engulfs tender strips of steak in this wonderful version of an old favorite.

1 Tbsp. olive oil
1 lb. beef round steak, trimmed and cut into ½-inch strips
Salt and pepper to taste
1 medium onion, diced
10-oz. package white mushrooms, wiped clean, stemmed, and halved

1 cup tomato sauce
8 drops Sweetleaf Stevia Grape
1 cup beef broth
½ cup unsweetened plain almond milk

1. Heat the oil in a large non-stick skillet over medium-high heat. Add the beef, season with salt and pepper, and cook, stirring occasionally, until lightly browned, about 5 minutes. Remove beef with a slotted spoon and set aside.
2. Add the onion to the skillet and cook, stirring often, until softened, about 3 minutes. Add the mushrooms to the skillet and cook 2 minutes more.
3. Stir in the tomato sauce, Stevia, and broth, bring to a boil, add the browned beef, and reduce the heat to low. Cover and cook until beef is fork tender, about 1 hour. Occasionally stir to prevent sticking.
4. Use a slotted spoon to transfer the meat and mushrooms to a warm serving bowl. Add the almond milk to the skillet and whisk to combine. Allow to simmer and thicken for 2 minutes. Taste the sauce for seasoning and pour over the beef and mushrooms. Serve immediately.

Makes 4 servings (270 calories; 13 grams fat, 29 grams protein, 8 grams carbohydrates)

M1 Caution Modification: Replace the almond milk with light or regular sour cream.

M2/Life Modification: Serve with ½ cup cooked egg noodles per serving.

Winter Beef Stew

Guaranteed to warm you from head to toe, this comforting and delicious stew can also be used as a great base for a potpie in Life Maintenance.

2 Tbsp. coconut or olive oil

1 lb. stewing beef, cubed and trimmed of excess fat

Salt and pepper to taste

1 medium onion, chopped

1 large celery stalk, chopped

2 garlic cloves, minced

1 Tbsp. tomato paste

2 cups beef broth

1 cup water

10 drops Sweetleaf Stevia Grape

1 bay leaf

2 large carrots, peeled and cut into 1-inch chunks

2 medium turnips, peeled and quartered

1 Tbsp. fresh parsley, chopped

1. Heat oil in a large heavy-bottomed pot over medium-high heat. Season beef with salt and pepper, and fry in the oil until browned on all sides, 5 to 7 minutes. Remove beef from pot and set aside.
2. Add onion and celery to pot and cook over medium heat, stirring often, until softened, about 4 minutes. Add garlic and cook another minute.
3. Stir in tomato paste and continue to cook, stirring constantly, for 2 minutes. Add broth, water, Stevia, and bay leaf, increase heat to high, and bring to a boil. Return beef to pot, reduce heat to medium-low, and simmer, covered, until nearly fork tender, about 1½ hours.
4. Add carrots and cook at a simmer for 15 minutes. Add turnips and cook, stirring occasionally, until beef and all vegetables are completely tender, 20 to 30 minutes. Add water, if necessary, to prevent sticking and to maintain gravy consistency. Serve immediately topped with the parsley.

Makes 4 servings (330 calories; 23 grams fat, 25 grams protein, 10 grams carbohydrates)

M1 Caution Modification: Add ¼ cup fresh or frozen green peas during the last 10 minutes of cooking.

M2/Life Modification: Add 1 medium peeled potato, cut into chunks, when adding the turnips.

Beef Skewers with Peanut Satay

A tangy peanut butter flavored sauce and butter leaf lettuce leaves for wrapping accompany these quickly grilled, tender morsels of beef.

For the Sauce:

¼ cup low-sodium soy sauce or Bragg Liquid Aminos
¼ cup cottage cheese
2 Tbsp. beef broth

Juice of ½ a lemon
6 drops Capella Peanut Butter
12 drops Clear Stevia
Dash Frank's Hot Sauce

For the Beef:

8 oz. beef tenderloin or sirloin steak, cut into long, thin strips
Salt and pepper to taste
¼ tsp. curry powder
1 small head Boston Lettuce, core removed, leaves separated, washed and dried

½ bunch green onions, chopped
Oil for grilling
10 or 12 bamboo or metal skewers

1. Combine sauce ingredients in a blender and puree until smooth. Taste for seasoning and Stevia, transfer to a dipping bowl, and set aside.
2. Thread beef slices onto skewers. Season with salt and pepper and sprinkle lightly with curry powder.
3. Heat an indoor or outdoor grill to high and brush lightly with oil. Grill skewered beef until edges are brown, about 2 minutes per side. Transfer to a heated platter.
4. Serve immediately with the sauce, chopped green onions for sprinkling, and lettuce leaves for wrapping.

Makes 2 servings (280 calories; 16 grams fat, 29 grams protein, 6 grams carbohydrates)

M1 Caution Modification: Replace the cottage cheese with peanut butter and reduce Stevia to 3 drops.

M2/Life Modification: Serve cooked rice noodles along with other fillings for the wraps.

Veal Chops with Summer Vegetable Ragout

Tender veal rests on a flavorful bed of fresh farm vegetable sauté in this easy, but elegant, presentation.

2 Tbsp. olive oil
2 6-oz. rib veal chops on the bone
Salt and pepper to taste
¼ tsp. ground cumin
1 shallot, minced
½ medium red bell pepper, diced small
1 small zucchini, trimmed and diced small

½ cup chicken broth
4 or 5 drops Capella Butter
6 drops Clear Stevia
Dash paprika
6 cherry tomatoes, halved
¼ cup fresh basil, torn

1. Heat 1 tablespoon of oil in a large nonstick skillet over medium-high heat. Season chops on both sides with salt, pepper, and cumin and cook until brown, about 3 minutes per side. Transfer to a plate and set aside.
2. Add remaining tablespoon of oil to skillet, add shallot and bell pepper, and cook, stirring often, until softened, about 3 minutes. Stir in zucchini and cook another minute.
3. Combine broth with Capella and Stevia and add with paprika to the skillet. Return chops to skillet, cover, and cook over low heat until veal is no longer pink, about 5 minutes. Transfer chops to serving dishes, add tomatoes and basil to the pan, stir for 1 minute to heat through, and spoon ragout over veal chops. Serve immediately.

Makes 2 servings (440 calories; 32 grams fat, 30 grams protein, 5 grams carbohydrates)

M1 Caution Modification: Reduce Capella drops to 2, and swirl in 2 tsp. unsalted butter before spooning the ragout.

M2/Life Modification: Add ⅔ cup fresh corn kernels when adding the zucchini.

Parma-Style Veal Marinara

A popular Italian entrée gets an easy makeover in this delectable version made with homemade sauce and some terrific upgrades.

4 veal cutlets (1 lb. total)
1 Tbsp. olive oil
Salt and pepper to taste
3 Tbsp. olive oil
2 large eggs, beaten

6 drops Sweetleaf Stevia Lemon Drop
1½ cups Homemade Marinara Sauce (see page 193)
½ cup large curd cottage cheese

1. Preheat the oven to 350° F.
2. Gently pound cutlets to ⅛-inch thickness between 2 pieces of waxed paper. Season both sides with salt and pepper.
3. Place beaten eggs in a shallow bowl and stir in the Stevia. Heat the olive oil in a large nonstick skillet. Dip veal, one cutlet at a time, into egg, allow excess to drip off, and place carefully in the hot oil.
4. Fry cutlets until golden brown, about 3 minutes per side. Transfer to a large baking dish and pour marinara sauce over. Place a dollop of the cottage cheese over each cutlet and bake until sauce is bubbly and cheese has begun to brown, 10 to 12 minutes. Serve immediately.

Makes 4 servings (360 calories; 23 grams fat, 25 grams protein, 6 grams carbohydrates)

M1 Caution Modification: Replace cottage cheese with shredded mozzarella cheese.

M2/Life Modification: Dip cutlets in whole grain breadcrumbs after egg mixture and fry as above.

Pork Chops with Apples and Kraut

This terrific dish with chunky sweet apples is a snap to make and super delectable to eat as well.

2 Tbsp. olive oil

8 thin-cut loin or rib pork chops (1 lb. total)

Salt and pepper to taste

2 large Red or Golden Delicious apples, cored and cut into eighths

Dash of cinnamon

15-oz. can of sauerkraut, drained

¼ cup chicken broth

4 drops Capella Apple Pie

5 drops Clear Stevia

1. Preheat the oven to 375° F.
2. Heat the oil in a nonstick skillet over medium-high heat. Season pork chops with salt and pepper and fry in skillet until lightly browned, about 2 minutes per side. Transfer to a 9 x 13-inch casserole dish.
3. Add apples to skillet, sprinkle with cinnamon, and cook, scraping up browned bits, for 2 minutes, just until they begin to color. Transfer to the edges of the casserole.
4. Add sauerkraut to skillet and cook, stirring, until heated through, about 3 minutes. Combine broth, Capella, and Stevia in a small bowl and pour over the sauerkraut, stirring well to combine. Remove from the heat and place the mixture on top of the pork chops in the casserole to cover.
5. Bake until pork chops are no longer pink and apples are brown and fork tender, about 35 minutes. Serve immediately.

Makes 4 servings (375 calories; 19 grams fat, 20 grams protein, 16 grams carbohydrates)

M1 Caution Modification: Eliminate olive oil and fry 4 slices of bacon in the skillet. When crisp, set aside and use the bacon drippings to fry the pork chops.

M2/Life Modification: Add 2 medium peeled Idaho potatoes, cut into eighths, when adding the apples.

Pork Tenderloin with Blueberry Sauce

Pork always pairs well with fruit and here it teams up with luscious blueberries for a wonderful entrée that is simple and satisfying.

1 Tbsp. coconut or olive oil	½ cup water
1 unseasoned pork tenderloin (1 to 1½ lbs.)	6 drops Capella Blueberry
Salt and pepper to taste	8 drops Clear Stevia, or more to taste
Dash ground coriander	1 tsp. fresh parsley, chopped
2 cups blueberries, fresh or frozen	1 tsp. fresh thyme, chopped
Juice of ½ a lemon	1 tsp. fresh sage, chopped

1. Preheat the oven to 400° F.
2. Heat the oil in a large nonstick skillet over medium-high heat. Season the tenderloin with salt, pepper, and the coriander and brown in the skillet on all sides. Transfer to a medium roasting pan and place in the oven to finish cooking for 20 to 25 minutes or until an internal read thermometer reaches 140° F.
3. Meanwhile, combine the remaining ingredients, except for the chopped herbs, in the same skillet and cook over medium-low heat, stirring often, until the berries begin to break down and create a sauce-like consistency. Stir in the herbs, set aside, and keep warm.
4. When the tenderloin is done, allow to rest on a cutting board for 10 minutes before slicing and serving with the sauce.

Makes 4 servings (250 calories; 6 grams fat, 28 grams protein, 12 grams carbohydrates)

M1 Caution Modification: Replace the water with orange juice and/or swirl in 1 tsp. of unsalted butter before serving the sauce.

M2/Life Modification: Replace the water with blueberry/pomegranate juice.

Holiday Ham Steak with Redeye Gravy

Capella Cherry Cola adds just the right amount of sweetness to this classic dish that's quick and easy to make.

1 tsp. olive oil

1 single serve (about 4 oz.) pre-cooked ham steak

Fresh ground pepper

2 Tbsp. canned cherries, no syrup/sugar, diced

½ cup cold coffee

4 or 5 drops Capella Cherry Cola

6 to 8 drops Clear Stevia, or more to taste

1 tsp. fresh parsley, finely chopped

1. Heat the oil in a nonstick skillet over medium-high heat. Add the ham steak, season with pepper, and brown lightly on each side for about 2 minutes.
2. Stir in the cherries and cook, stirring, another minute.
3. In a small bowl, combine the coffee with the Capella and Stevia. Pour into the skillet, stir, reduce the heat to low, and cover. Continue to cook until the ham is heated through and the sauce is slightly thickened, about 2 minutes more.
4. Transfer to a dinner plate, spoon sauce over top, sprinkle with the parsley, and serve immediately.

Makes 1 serving (250 calories; 11 grams fat, 20 grams protein, 6 grams carbohydrates)

M1 Modification: Stir in 1 Tbsp. of dark seedless raisins with the cherries.

M2/Life Modification: Replace olive oil with butter.

Greek Minted Lamb Chops

Broiled or grilled, these marinated chops are super delicious with the flavor of mint and Mediterranean herbs.

For the Marinade:

2 Tbsp. olive oil	1 Tbsp. fresh mint leaves, chopped
Juice of 1 lemon	1 tsp. fresh oregano, chopped
1 large garlic clove, minced	1 tsp. fresh marjoram, chopped
4 drops Capella Cool Mint	1 tsp. fresh basil, chopped

For the Lamp Chops:

6 small rib lamb chops, trimmed of excess fat	Salt and pepper to taste
	Lemon wedges

1. In a shallow dish, combine the marinade ingredients, stirring well. Place the chops in the marinade and refrigerate for at least 1 hour, turning halfway through.
2. Heat an indoor or outdoor grill or broiler to medium-high. Pat dry the chops and season with salt and pepper. Grill or broil to desired doneness, about 3 minutes per side for medium-rare. Transfer to a serving dish and serve with the lemon wedges.

Makes 2 servings (450 calories; 10 grams fat, 15 grams protein, 2 grams carbohydrates)

M1 Caution Modification: Serve with a dollop of Cucumber Raita (see page 191).

M2/Life Modification: Serve over ½ cup cooked orzo.

Loin Lamb Chops with Apricot Mustard Glaze

Sweet and tangy is the name of the game in this easy entrée that's made in the skillet for a quick and delicious dinner.

For the Glaze:

2 fresh apricots, pitted and roughly chopped

¼ cup water

10 drops Sweetleaf Stevia Apricot Nectar

2 Tbsp. hot prepared mustard

For the Lamb Chops:

1 Tbsp. olive oil

4 medium loin lamb chops

Salt and pepper to taste

1 Tbsp. fresh parsley, roughly chopped

1. Prepare the glaze by combining the ingredients in a blender or mini chopper and processing until smooth. Transfer to a bowl and set aside.
2. Heat the oil in a large nonstick skillet over medium-high heat. Season the chops with salt and pepper and brown well, about 2 minutes per side. Reduce the heat to low and cover.
3. Every minute or so, brush the chops with the glaze and turn them over until desired doneness is reached, about 5 minutes for medium.
4. Transfer to a platter and top with the remaining glaze, if any, and the chopped parsley before serving.

Makes 2 servings (320 calories; 17 grams fat, 30 grams protein, 4 grams carbohydrates)

M1 Caution Modification: Replace the apricots with diced mango.

M2/Life Modification: Replace the water with apricot or mango nectar.

FISH AND SHELLFISH ENTRÉES

MAINTENANCE

HEALTHY FISH AND SEAFOOD selections make great dinner entrées for Maintenance meals. With the help of Capella and Stevia, the flavor possibilities are endless. From zesty broiled filets to creamy coconut Thai shrimp, you'll have no trouble finding a recipe to enjoy during this phase of the HCG Protocol.

As with all Maintenance recipes, monitor both your "Caution" selections and calorie counts as you progress each week. Be sure to only introduce your allotted sugars and starches when allowed. Although the calorie counts given are as accurate as possible, please consult the nutritional labels of the specific products used to be sure.

Seared Ahi Tuna with Wasabi Dressing
(Recipe on page 232)

Lemon-Lime Scrod with Salsa

Prepared salsa makes this dish a real snap while the tang of citrus wakes up the terrific Mexican spices.

8-oz. scrod or cod filet, cut into 2 pieces
Juice of 1 lime
8 drops Sweetleaf Stevia Lemon Drop
Dash ground cumin
Dash chili powder
Salt and pepper to taste
½ cup purchased tomato salsa
1 Tbsp. fresh cilantro, chopped

1. Preheat the broiler and position the oven rack 4 to 5 inches below the flame.
2. On an aluminum foil-lined baking sheet that has been lightly coated with cooking spray or oil, place the fish in a single layer. Combine the lime juice and Stevia and drizzle over the fish. Sprinkle with the cumin and chili powder, and season with salt and pepper.
3. Broil, shifting the pan a few times to cook evenly, until the fish is firm to the touch and golden brown around the edges, 5 to 6 minutes.
4. Remove from the broiler, transfer to warm serving plates, and spoon the salsa evenly over the fish, garnishing with the cilantro. Serve immediately.

Makes 2 servings (125 calories; 1 gram fat, 21 grams protein, 4 grams carbohydrates)

M1 Caution Modification: Stir ¼ cup diced fresh mango into the prepared salsa before serving.

M2/Life Modification: Stir 2 Tbsp. cooked corn kernels and 2 Tbsp. black beans into the salsa before serving.

Sensational Salmon Burger

This healthy and delicious alternative to the classic burger is perfect for the grill or broiler.

8 oz. boneless, skinless, salmon filet, cut into large cubes
Salt and pepper to taste
1 large egg white, slightly beaten
1 Tbsp. lemon juice
4 drops Sweetleaf Stevia Valencia Orange

4 drops Sweetleaf Stevia Lemon Drop
¼ tsp. Old Bay Seasoning
2 tsp. fresh dill, chopped
2 tsp. fresh cilantro, chopped

1. Place all the ingredients in a food processor and, using the pulse button, chop until just combined. Transfer to a cutting board or clean plate. Mold the salmon mixture into the shape of 2 burgers, place on waxed paper, and set in the fridge for 10 to 15 minutes.
2. Heat a grill or broiler to medium-high. Lightly coat the grates or the bottom of a broiler pan with oil. Grill or broil the burgers until they are firm to the touch and lightly golden, 3 to 4 minutes per side. Serve immediately.

Makes 2 servings (220 calories; 16 grams fat, 24 grams protein)

M1 Caution Modification: Serve with a dollop of Quick Tartar Sauce (see page 192).

M2/Life Modification: Serve on a low-carb burger bun.

Roasted Salmon with Sweet Mustard Glaze

Stevia provides the "sweet" in this easy-to-make oven-roasted salmon dish that's delicious with a side of sautéed spinach.

2 Tbsp. mustard
10 to 12 drops Sweetleaf Stevia Apricot Nectar
1 Tbsp. coconut or olive oil

1 Tbsp. fresh dill sprigs, chopped
Salt and pepper to taste
2 4-oz. salmon filets, skin and any remaining pin bones removed

1. Preheat the oven to 375° F.
2. In a small mixing bowl, whisk together the mustard, Stevia, oil, and dill. Place the salmon filets in a zippered plastic bag, add the mustard glaze, seal, and turn to coat the filets with the sauce. Set aside for 20 minutes.
3. Place the salmon filets in a single layer in the middle of a medium roasting pan, spread any remaining glaze over the filets, and roast until browned around the edges and firm to the touch, about 25 minutes. Serve immediately.

Makes 2 servings (220 calories; 15 grams fat, 24 grams protein, 0 grams carbohydrates)

M1 Caution Modification: Add 2 Tbsp. apricot juice to the glaze while whisking.

M2/Life Modification: Cut 2 medium unpeeled red potatoes into ¼-inch-thick rounds and spread out evenly in the pan, lightly coating with oil. Roast for 15 minutes before adding the salmon filets and continue as above. Turn potatoes to brown evenly.

Tilapia with Teriyaki Vegetables

Tender tilapia absorbs the delicious flavor of teriyaki sauce and highlights this easy Asian-style dinner that's both healthy and satisfying.

1 lb. tilapia filets	1 cup small broccoli florets
1 cup low-sodium soy sauce or Bragg Liquid Aminos	1 large celery stalk, trimmed and thinly sliced on the diagonal
2 Tbsp. rice vinegar	1 medium carrot, thinly sliced on the diagonal
¼ tsp. Clear Stevia	
1 Tbsp. minced fresh ginger	8 green onions, cut into 2-inch pieces
1 large garlic clove, minced	
2 Tbsp. coconut or olive oil	1 cup snow peas

1. In a shallow bowl, combine soy sauce, vinegar, Stevia, ginger, and garlic. Place fish, flesh side down, in soy mixture and marinate in the refrigerator for 30 minutes. Preheat the oven to 350° F.
2. Heat 1 tablespoon of oil in a large nonstick skillet over medium-high heat. Reserving the marinade, carefully brown the tilapia in the skillet without cooking through and transfer to a baking dish. Bake in the oven until opaque in center, about 8 minutes.
3. Meanwhile, add remaining tablespoon of oil to skillet and heat to nearly smoking. Add broccoli, celery, and carrots and stir-fry for 3 minutes. Add green onions and snow peas and stir-fry another 2 minutes.
4. Add reserved marinade, stir well, reduce heat to medium-low, and cook until vegetables are crisp tender and marinade has thickened into a glaze, about 3 minutes more.
5. To serve, transfer tilapia to a platter and spoon the vegetables on top and around.

Makes 4 servings (220 calories; 9 grams fat, 25 grams protein, 7 grams carbohydrates)

M1 Caution Modification: Add 4 oz. sliced shiitake mushrooms with the snow peas.

M2/Life Modification: Serve with ½ cup rice per serving.

Perfect Piña Colada Mahi-Mahi

Hawaii beckons in this fabulous preparation for firm and tasty Mahi-Mahi with fruity, fresh flavor.

2 4-oz. Mahi-Mahi filets
1½ cups unsweetened almond milk
8 to 10 drops Capella with Stevia Piña Colada
½ cup fresh pineapple chunks

Dash paprika
1 Tbsp. coconut or olive oil
Salt and pepper to taste
Fresh pineapple for garnish (optional)

1. Combine the almond milk, Capella, pineapple, and paprika in a blender and puree until smooth. Place the fish filets in a rimmed dish and cover with the milk mixture. Cover and marinate in the refrigerator, turning occasionally, for at least 1 hour.
2. Heat the oil in a nonstick skillet of medium-high heat. Pat dry the filets, reserving the marinade, and season them with salt and pepper. Brown the filets in the skillet, 2 minutes per side, reduce the heat to low, cover, and continue to cook until firm, about 4 minutes. Transfer to a warm dish and set aside.
3. Pour the reserved marinade into the skillet, increase the heat to high, and reduce liquid, stirring often, until slightly thick. Taste for seasoning, pour over the filets, garnish with pineapple if using, and serve immediately.

Make 2 servings (240 calories; 10 grams fat, 23 grams protein, 8 grams carbohydrates)

M1 Caution Modification: Replace half the almond milk with unsweetened coconut milk.

M2/Life Modification: Top with chopped macadamia nuts and/or serve with ½ cup rice.

Seared Ahi Tuna with Wasabi Dressing

Fans of sashimi will adore this easy preparation for tuna made with the zing of wasabi and the zest of orange.

2 tsp. wasabi powder, more or less to taste

1 Tbsp. hot water

2 Tbsp. low-sodium soy sauce or Bragg Liquid Aminos

Juice of ½ an orange

8 drops Sweetleaf Stevia Valencia Orange

1 Tbsp. olive oil

2 4-oz. Ahi or sushi-grade tuna filets

Salt and pepper to taste

2 cups watercress

1. In a small bowl, whisk together wasabi and water until smooth. Whisk in soy sauce, orange juice, and Stevia and set aside.
2. Lightly coat tuna filets with some of the oil, season with salt and pepper, and set aside.
3. Brush remaining oil in a nonstick skillet. Over high heat, cook tuna until crust is browned but fish is still pink inside, 2 to 3 minutes per side. Transfer to a cutting board.
4. To serve, scatter watercress over 2 plates, slice tuna, and place on top, then drizzle wasabi dressing over all.

Makes 2 servings (210 calories; 8 grams fat, 26 grams protein, 1 gram carbohydrates)

M1 Caution Modification: Sprinkle 2 Tbsp. sesame seeds over the filets before sautéing.

M2/Life Modification: Serve with ½ cup sticky rice.

Grilled Swordfish with Peach Salsa

Easy to prepare and terrific for outdoor dining, this grilled chicken dish with alkalizing peaches and greens will keep you satisfied and healthy.

For the Peach Salsa:

2 medium ripe peaches
½ cup Vidalia onion (or another sweet onion), chopped
1 small jalapeno pepper, trimmed, seeded, and finely chopped
2 Tbsp. freshly squeezed lime juice
3 or 4 drops Capella Peaches & Cream
1 Tbsp. fresh cilantro, finely chopped

For the Fish Steaks:

2 4-oz. swordfish steaks
Salt and pepper to taste
Oil for coating the grill

1. To make the salsa, bring a medium saucepan of water to boil over high heat. Drop in the peaches and cook for 30 seconds. Using a slotted spoon, submerge the peaches into a bowl of ice-cold water to cool. Remove and drain on paper towels. Using a sharp paring knife, peel the peaches, remove the pit, and cut into ¼-inch dices. In a medium mixing bowl, combine the peaches and the remaining ingredients and, using a rubber spatula, gently fold to combine. Taste for seasoning, cover, and chill.
2. Prepare an outdoor gas or charcoal barbecue for medium-high grilling. (Alternatively, preheat an indoor countertop grill or stovetop grill pan.) Lightly coat the grill with oil to prevent sticking.
3. Season both sides of the steaks with salt and pepper, and grill the filets until no longer pink, 3 to 5 minutes per side. Transfer to clean plates and serve topped with the peach salsa.

Makes 2 servings (225 calories; 5 grams fat, 25 grams protein, 19 grams carbohydrates)

M1 Caution Modification: Replace 1 peach with 1 cup cantaloupe diced into small pieces.

M2/Life Modification: Top the salsa with a dollop of plain or peach yogurt.

Mexican Fish Tacos

Easy to make and fun to eat, this rendition of a popular Tex-Mex entrée is made with lettuce wraps to hold the filling and can be later upgraded to include corn tacos.

1 Tbsp. coconut or olive oil

8 oz. firm flesh fish filets, such as haddock, cut into bite-sized chunks

Salt and pepper to taste

1 medium onion, sliced

1 red bell pepper, seeded and sliced

1 jalapeno pepper, seeded and chopped

1 tsp. chili powder

1 tsp. ground cumin

Juice of ½ a lime

3 or 4 drops Capella Coconut

1 Tbsp. fresh cilantro, chopped

4 large lettuce leaves

1. Heat oil in a large nonstick skillet over medium-high heat. Add fish chunks, season with salt and pepper, and cook, stirring often but carefully, until pieces are cooked through, about 3 minutes. Transfer to a bowl with a slotted spoon and set aside.
2. Add onion, bell pepper, and jalapeno pepper to skillet and cook over medium-high heat until somewhat softened, about 5 minutes. Return fish to skillet, sprinkle with chili powder and cumin, and cook, stirring often, just until heated through.
3. Remove from the heat. Combine the lime juice and Capella and sprinkle over the fish. Top with the cilantro.
4. To serve, spoon the fish mixture into the lettuce leaves and fold over taco-style.

Makes 2 servings (200 calories; 7 grams fat, 21 grams protein, 8 grams carbohydrates)

M1 Caution Modification: Top each "taco" with a dollop of sour cream.

M2/Life Modification: Replace the lettuce leaves with crisp corn taco shells.

Thai Coconut Shrimp

Deliciously creamy with a hint of sweet and a spicy kick, simple shrimp goes Thai in this easy and super flavorful dish.

2 tsp. coconut or olive oil
1 small onion, minced
1 garlic clove, minced
1 Tbsp. fresh ginger, finely chopped
½ tsp. turmeric
¼ tsp. ground coriander
1½ cups unsweetened plain almond milk
½ tsp. Frank's Hot Sauce, or more to taste

8 drops Capella Coconut
12 to 15 drops Clear Stevia
1 Tbsp. tomato paste
1 medium red bell pepper, cored, seeded, and cut into thin strips
1 handful baby spinach
1 lb. medium shrimp, peeled and deveined
1 tsp. lime juice
Salt and pepper to taste

1. Heat the oil in a medium pot over medium-high heat. Add the onion and cook, stirring often, until softened, about 2 minutes. Stir in the garlic, ginger, turmeric, and coriander, and cook another minute.
2. Whisk in the almond milk, hot sauce, Capella, Stevia, and tomato paste and bring to a boil. Reduce the heat to low and simmer for 4 minutes.
3. Add the bell pepper, spinach, and shrimp and cook, stirring often, over medium heat, until shrimp is pink and firm, about 5 minutes.
4. Add the lime juice and cook another minute. Taste for the addition of salt and pepper and serve immediately.

Makes 4 servings (223 calories; 6 grams fat, 25 grams protein, 8 grams carbohydrates)

M1 Caution Modification: Replace half the almond milk with unsweetened coconut milk.

M2/Life Modification: Serve over ½ cup basmati or jasmine rice.

Pan-Seared Scallops with Orange Glaze

Large, soft, and sweet scallops pair beautifully with the flavor of orange and ginger in this easy-to-prepare main dish.

1 Tbsp. olive oil

8 oz. sea scallops, rinsed and patted dry

Salt and pepper to taste

1 Tbsp. minced fresh ginger

6 green onions, cut into 2-inch pieces

½ cup sliced water chestnuts

Juice of 1 orange

8 drops Sweetleaf Stevia Valencia Orange

4 to 6 drops Capella Butter

1. Heat oil in a large nonstick skillet over medium-high heat. Season scallops with salt and pepper and quickly sear them in the hot skillet until lightly browned, about 2 minutes per side. Remove with tongs and set on a warm plate.
2. Add ginger and green onions to skillet and cook, stirring, over medium-high heat, until slightly softened, about 3 minutes. Add water chestnuts and stir another minute.
3. Stir in orange juice, Capella, and Stevia and bring to a simmer. Return scallops to skillet and stir well to coat. Cook another minute over low heat and serve immediately.

Makes 2 servings (240 calories; 7 grams fat, 21 grams protein, 16 grams carbohydrates)

M1 Caution Modification: Just before serving, swirl in 2 tsp. softened unsalted butter.

M2/Life Modification: Serve over ½ cup brown rice.

Thick and Rich Seafood Gumbo

This southern favorite features the flavors of the sea and a spicy tomato creole sauce.

1 lb. large shrimp, shelled and deveined

4 oz. baby scallops

4 oz. swordfish, cut into 1-inch cubes

1 tsp. creole-style seasoning blend

1 Tbsp. olive oil

1 medium onion, diced

1 medium green bell pepper, cored, seeded, and diced

1 medium celery stalk, trimmed and diced

Salt and pepper to taste

2 garlic cloves, minced

28-oz. can plum tomatoes, un-drained and roughly chopped

1 cup water

10 drops Sweetleaf Stevia Grape

1 Tbsp. tomato paste

½ tsp. dried oregano

1. In a large bowl, combine the shrimp, scallops, and swordfish, sprinkle with the creole seasoning and set aside.
2. Heat the oil in a heavy-bottomed pot over medium-high heat. Add the onion, green pepper, and celery. Season with salt and pepper, and cook over medium heat until the vegetables are softened, stirring often, about 4 minutes. Add the garlic and cook, stirring another minute.
3. Stir in the plum tomatoes and their liquid, the water, Stevia, tomato paste, and oregano and bring to a boil. Reduce heat to medium-low and simmer for 15 minutes, stirring occasionally.
4. Add the seafood, stir well, and simmer until just cooked, 3 to 4 minutes. Remove the seafood with a slotted spoon and transfer to a warm serving bowl.
5. Continue to simmer the sauce until well thickened, 5 to 8 minutes more. Taste for seasoning, pour over the cooked seafood, and serve immediately.

Makes 4 servings (275 calories; 6 grams fat, 36 grams protein, 13 grams carbohydrates)

M1 Caution Modification: Add ⅔ cup sliced fresh or frozen okra with the tomatoes.

M2/Life Modification: Make a roux with ¼ cup vegetable oil and ¼ cup all-purpose flour by whisking together the oil and flour in a medium glass bowl and microwaving on high for 3 minutes or until browned and fragrant. Replace the olive oil in Step 2 with this prepared roux.

VEGETARIAN AND SIDE DISHES

OR VEGETARIANS AND VEGANS, the HCG Protocol can pose challenges, but none that are impossible to conquer. During M1, most vegetarian protein selections are restricted to eggs, protein powder-based recipes, and cottage cheese, but moving into M2/Life phase, a terrific array of high-protein beans, grains, and vegetables are gradually allowed. You'll enjoy many of them in the recipes in this chapter, as well as a selection of great-tasting side dishes, all full of fabulous flavor with the aid of Capella and Stevia.

When vegetable broth is called for, feel free to use the broth recipe included in the VLCD soup section, or you may use a purchased version as well, provided it is low in sodium and carbs and has zero sugars.

As with all Maintenance recipes, monitor both your "Caution" selections and calorie counts as you progress each week. Be sure to only introduce your allotted sugars and starches when allowed. Although the calorie counts given are as accurate as possible, please consult the nutritional labels of the specific products used to be sure.

Ratatouille Casserole
(Recipe on page 242)

Indonesian Vegetable Stew

Exotic flavors highlight this medley of nutritious vegetables that has a good amount of heat for spicy food lovers.

1 Tbsp. coconut or olive oil
½ medium onion, chopped
½ medium red bell pepper, cored, seeded, and diced
Salt and pepper to taste
1 Tbsp. minced fresh ginger
2 garlic cloves, minced
½ small jalapeno pepper (or more to taste), seeded and minced
1 Tbsp. curry powder
½ tsp. ground turmeric

¼ tsp. coriander
2 cups Basic Vegetable Broth (see page 22)
½ cup unsweetened plain almond milk
6 drops Capella Coconut
8 drops Clear Stevia
1 cup cauliflower florets
½ cup carrots, sliced
½ cup snap peas

1. Heat the oil in a large pot over medium-high heat. Add the onion, bell pepper, salt, and pepper and cook, stirring often, until softened, about 3 minutes.
2. Add the ginger, garlic, and jalapeno and cook, stirring, another minute. Add the curry powder, turmeric, and coriander and stir well to coat the vegetables.
3. Stir in the broth, almond milk, Capella, and Stevia and bring to a low boil. Add the cauliflower, carrots, and snap peas, reduce the heat to low, cover, and simmer until the vegetables are tender, 12 to 15 minutes.
4. When the vegetables are cooked, remove them with a slotted spoon to a serving bowl. Taste the sauce for seasoning and adjust if necessary. Simmer to reduce slightly, then pour over the vegetables and serve.

Makes 2 servings (215 calories; 7 grams protein, 8 grams fat, 12 grams carbohydrates)

M1 Caution Modification: Add ½ cup edamame (fresh soybeans) with the cauliflower and other vegetables and/or whisk in ¼ cup plain yogurt into the sauce before serving.

M2/Life Modification: Serve over ½ cup brown basmati rice.

Ratatouille Casserole

The herbs of Provence waft through the kitchen as this delectable, colorful, and hearty casserole bakes and bubbles.

2 Tbsp. olive oil

2 medium zucchini, cut into ½-inch rounds

1 medium yellow squash, cut into ½-inch rounds

1 large green bell pepper, seeded and cut into 1-inch pieces

2 small red onions, cut into ¼-inch rounds

2 small eggplant, left unpeeled and cut into ½-inch rounds

4 plum tomatoes, cut into ½-inch rounds

Salt and pepper to taste

2 tsp. Herbs de Provence

½ cup Basic Vegetable Broth (see page 22)

8 drops Sweetleaf Stevia Grape

1. Preheat the oven to 350° F. Lightly coat a shallow oval or rectangular 1½-quart baking dish with a little of the olive oil.
2. Layer the vegetables in rows, domino fashion, staggering them to distribute the different vegetables throughout. Season with salt and pepper and sprinkle the herbs over.
3. Stir together the broth and Stevia drops and pour around the edges of the casserole and drizzle the remaining olive oil over the top.
4. Bake until vegetables are fork tender, most of the liquid has evaporated, and the top is lightly golden, about 45 minutes. Allow to rest for 10 minutes before serving.

Makes 4 servings (190 calories; 4 grams protein, 7 grams fat, 20 grams carbohydrates)

M1 Caution Modification: Top with ½ cup shredded Parmesan cheese before baking.

M2/Life Modification: Top with ½ cup whole grain bread crumbs before baking.

Eggplant Rollatini

This hearty vegetarian Italian dish is baked and not fried for a lower fat and cleaner taste that you'll absolutely love.

1 large eggplant	1 large egg, slightly beaten
2 Tbsp. olive oil	4 to 6 drops Sweetleaf Stevia Lemon Drop
Salt and pepper to taste	
1 cup large curd cottage cheese	1½ cups Homemade Marinara Sauce (see page 193)
1 tsp. fresh parsley, chopped	

1. Preheat the oven to 350° F. Lightly brush a large baking sheet with some of the oil and set aside.
2. Cut the ends off the eggplant and peel. Slicing downward, cut into ¼-inch slices to make 4 to 6 complete slices (discard end pieces or reserve for another recipe). Place the eggplant on the oiled sheet and brush with more of the oil. Sprinkle with salt and pepper and bake until fork tender and lightly browned around the edges, about 25 minutes, turning halfway through and brushing with more oil as needed. Set aside to cool.
3. In a medium bowl, combine the cottage cheese, parsley, egg, Stevia, salt, and pepper. Lay the cooked eggplant slices on a flat surface and distribute the cheese filling among the slices by placing a dollop in the middle of each. Beginning at the short end of the slice, roll up the eggplant carefully but firmly to enclose the filling.
4. Spoon half the marinara sauce in the bottom of a medium casserole and place the roll ups, seam-side down, in the dish next to each other, but not touching. Pour the remaining sauce over all and bake until the sauce is bubbly and the filling is hot, about 20 minutes. Serve immediately.

Makes 2 servings (350 calories; 21 grams fat, 21 grams protein, 30 grams carbohydrates)

M1 Caution Modification: Replace the cottage cheese with ricotta cheese and/ or top the rollatini with ½ cup shredded mozzarella cheese before baking.

M2/Life Modification: Serve with a whole grain ciabatta roll or ½ cup whole wheat linguine.

Roasted Vegetable Mélange

This wonderful medley of flavorful veggies with a distinct hint of orange and thyme makes for a satisfying meatless meal or a terrific side dish for simply prepared chicken or fish.

½ medium head cauliflower, leaves removed

1 small yellow squash, ends trimmed and cut into ½-inch-thick rounds

1 pound fresh asparagus, woody bottoms removed

1 cup frozen artichoke hearts, thawed

½ medium red or orange bell pepper, seeded and cut into ½-inch strips

4 fresh thyme sprigs

¼ cup olive oil

8 drops Sweetleaf Stevia Valencia Orange

¼ tsp. orange zest

½ tsp. garlic salt

Salt and pepper to taste

1. Preheat the oven to 375° F.
2. Remove 1 inch from the cauliflower stalk, keeping the rest to hold the florets together. Using a large knife, cut the cauliflower into ¼-inch-thick slices so that they will lay flat. Place in a roasting pan with the squash, asparagus, artichoke, bell pepper, and thyme sprigs.
3. In a small bowl, whisk together the remaining ingredients, pour over the vegetables, and toss well to coat. Roast in the oven, occasionally shaking the pan to brown evenly, 25 to 30 minutes. Use a metal spatula halfway through to turn over the cauliflower and squash slices.
4. When the vegetables are lightly browned and fork tender, remove from the oven, sprinkle with additional salt and pepper, if desired, and serve from the roasting pan.

Makes 4 servings (215 calories; 13 grams fat, 4 grams protein, 9 grams carbohydrates)

M1 Caution Modification: During the last 10 minutes, sprinkle ½ cup shredded Parmesan cheese over the vegetables.

M2/Life Modification: Add 1 cup canned chickpeas, drained and rinsed, when roasting and/or serve over ½ cup brown rice.

Spanish-Style Grilled Leeks and Fennel

The piquant and zesty flavor of a classic Spanish sauce is the highlight of this smoky, grilled vegetable dish that's a real keeper.

2 large or 4 baby leeks
1 large fennel bulb, trimmed of stalks
2 Tbsp. olive oil

6 drops Sweetleaf Stevia Lemon Drop
Salt and pepper to taste
½ cup Romesco Sauce (see page 194)

1. Trim the ends of the leeks, removing most of the tough green part. Cut in half lengthwise and rinse under water to remove any grit. Cut the fennel bulb into quarters, trimming away tough leaves and most of the core.
2. Steam the leeks and fennel in a vegetable steamer or in the microwave until slightly fork tender. Transfer to a bowl and drizzle with the oil and Stevia. Season with salt and pepper and toss gently. Set aside.
3. Heat an outdoor grill to medium-high and grill the leeks and fennel until nicely grill marked and tender, about 10 minutes. Serve immediately with the Romesco sauce.

Makes 2 servings (295 calories; 14 grams fat, 5 grams protein, 41 grams carbohydrates)

M1 Caution Modification: After grilling, sprinkle the vegetables with ¼ cup crumbled Manchego cheese.

M2/Life Modification: Serve with ⅓ cup whole wheat couscous.

Crustless Quiche with Sun-Dried Tomatoes

No crust? No problem! This great tasting dish is easy to upgrade and completely meatless for vegetarian eaters.

1 tsp. olive oil
½ cup whipped cottage cheese
4 large eggs
⅔ cup unsweetened plain almond milk
6 drops Sweetleaf Stevia Vanilla Crème

Salt and pepper to taste
Dash nutmeg
½ tsp. Herbs de Provence
¼ cup sun-dried tomatoes (not marinated), minced

1. Preheat the oven to 350° F. Lightly coat an 8- or 9-inch round cake pan with the oil.
2. In a medium bowl, whisk together the remaining ingredients and pour into the prepared cake pan. Bake until the quiche is set and lightly browned on top, 25 to 30 minutes. Cut into quarters and serve.

Makes 4 servings (230 calories; 10 grams fat, 10 grams protein, 5 grams carbohydrates)

M1 Caution Modification: Add ½ cup shredded Jarlsberg or Swiss cheese to the mixture.

M2/Life Modification: Replace the cottage cheese with soft plain tofu.

Herbed Portobello Burger

Mushroom lovers adore the meatiness of a Portobello mushroom cap and here it fills in nicely for the standard beef burger, flavored with bold and aromatic herbs.

1 large Portobello mushroom cap, stem removed

1 Tbsp. olive oil

1 tsp. tarragon vinegar

3 drops Capella Cool Mint

1 tsp. fresh mint, finely chopped

1 tsp. fresh parsley, finely chopped

1 tsp. fresh tarragon, finely chopped

1 tsp. fresh basil, finely chopped

Salt and pepper to taste

Sweet and Spicy Sauce (see page 195)

Lettuce leaves and sliced tomato

1. Using a teaspoon, carefully scrape away the dark gills under the mushroom cap. In a small bowl, stir together the remaining ingredients.
2. Prepare an outdoor or indoor grill to medium-high. Grill the mushroom cap, brushing with the oil mixture, until fork tender, about 5 minutes. Transfer to a serving dish and top with the sauce, lettuce, and tomato.

Makes 1 serving (162 calories; 14 grams fat, 2 grams protein, 4 grams carbohydrates)

M1 Caution Modification: Melt 1 slice of your favorite cheese on top.

M2/Life Modification: Serve with a dollop of sour cream and/or a low-carb or whole grain burger bun.

Oven-Glazed Baby Carrots

A great side dish for any protein selection, baby carrots sweeten up naturally when roasted, along with a little help from Stevia!

16-oz. bag peeled baby carrots
1 Tbsp. olive oil
Salt and pepper to taste
⅓ cup currants

¼ cup fresh cranberries
Juice of 1 orange
8 drops Sweetleaf Stevia Berry

1. Preheat the oven to 375° F.
2. Place carrots in a medium roasting pan, add oil, salt, and pepper and toss to coat.
3. Roast in the oven until nearly fork tender, about 15 minutes. Stir in currants and cranberries. Combine orange juice and Stevia and pour over all. Continue roasting until carrots are cooked through and fruit is plump, about 10 to 15 minutes more. Serve immediately.

Makes 4 servings (88 calories; 3 grams fat, 1 gram protein, 14 grams carbohydrates)

M1 Caution Modification: Add 2 Tbsp. chopped pecans during last 5 minutes.

M2/Life Modification: Add 1 medium peeled and diced sweet potato after first 10 minutes of roasting.

Creole-Style Green Beans

Here's a vegetable dish to wake up your palate and add some zip to any meal in spiced-up and classically creole style.

Pinch salt

1 pound fresh green beans, ends trimmed

3 Tbsp. olive oil

1 small onion, chopped

1 small celery stalk, ends trimmed and diced

1 garlic clove, peeled and minced

1 small fresh chili pepper, seeded and minced

15-oz. can diced tomatoes, not drained

1 cup water

8 drops Sweetleaf Stevia Grape

Salt to taste

1. Bring a medium pot of water to a boil, add the salt, and cook the green beans until crisp tender, 10 to 12 minutes. Drain and set aside.
2. Heat the oil in a large skillet, add the onion and celery and cook, stirring, over medium-high heat until softened, 6 to 8 minutes. Add the garlic and chili pepper and cook another minute.
3. Add the green beans, tomatoes, water, and Stevia, bring to a simmer, and cook, stirring occasionally, until much of the liquid has been absorbed and the beans are fork tender.
4. Taste for the addition of salt and serve immediately.

Makes 4 servings (185 calories; 11 grams fat, 5 grams protein, 16 grams carbohydrates)

M1 Caution Modification: Stir in 1 cup cooked okra with the green beans.

M2/Life Modification: Stir in 1 cup cooked black-eyed peas with the green beans.

Lemony Brussels Sprouts

These tiny little cabbages get a boost of terrific flavor from both lemon and orange in this easy side dish.

1 lb. Brussels sprouts, trimmed and halved through the core

2 Tbsp. olive oil

Salt and pepper to taste

Juice of ½ a lemon

Juice of ½ an orange

4 drops Sweetleaf Stevia Valencia Orange

4 drops Sweetleaf Stevia Lemon Drop

1. Bring a medium saucepan of water to the boil. Add Brussels sprouts and simmer until fork tender, but not mushy, about 6 minutes. Drain and set aside.
2. Heat the oil in a skillet over medium heat, add Brussels sprouts and salt and pepper to taste. Combine the juices and Stevia and pour over the sprouts. Stir well to coat and cook, covered, until piping hot, about 2 minutes. Serve immediately.

Makes 4 servings (120 calories; 7 grams fat, 3 grams protein, 12 grams carbohydrates)

M1 Caution Modification: Replace the olive oil with unsalted butter.

M2/Life Modification: Add ½ cup chopped roasted chestnuts and/or ½ cup dried cranberries.

MAINTENANCE DESSERTS

OMETHING SWEET is always welcome after a meal—and sometimes in between! Here you'll find some delicious recipe ideas for satisfying that sweet craving. From yummy fruit-based desserts to refreshing frozen concoctions, there's no limit to the array of flavors you will enjoy thanks to the decadent flavors of Capella and Stevia.

As with all Maintenance recipes, monitor both your "Caution" selections and calorie counts as you progress each week. Be sure to only introduce your allotted sugars and starches when allowed. Although the calorie counts given are as accurate as possible, please consult the nutritional labels of the specific products used to be sure.

Mini Flourless Chocolate Torte
(Recipe on page 264)

Frozen Desserts

French Vanilla Ice Cream

Amazing but true, you'll love this rendition of a creamy vanilla frozen dessert that can be creatively flavored with any Capella or Stevia. Try Caramel, Banana, or even Cinnamon!

2 cups plain unsweetened almond milk
½ tsp. Clear Stevia

6 to 8 drops Capella French Vanilla
4 large egg yolks, at room temperature

1. In a medium saucepan, combine the almond milk, Stevia, and Capella. Bring to a simmer, whisking occasionally, over medium heat. Set aside.
2. In a medium mixing bowl, using an electric mixer on medium speed, beat the egg yolks until pale ribbons form when the beaters are lifted.
3. Slowly add half the milk mixture to the egg mixture, whisking well. Pour into the remaining milk in the saucepan and cook over medium-low heat, stirring constantly, until the mixture thickens somewhat and is able to coat the back of a spoon.
4. Immediately pour through a fine sieve into a bowl, cover the top with plastic wrap, and cool for 10 minutes. Chill in the refrigerator for at least 1 hour or until very cold.
5. Pour into an ice cream maker and, following the manufacturer's instructions, churn until thick and creamy. *Alternatively, pour the mixture into a 9 x 13-inch metal pan, place in the freezer, and whisk or stir, every 15 minutes, until thick and creamy.*
6. Transfer to an airtight container and keep frozen for up to 5 days.

Makes 4 servings (75 calories; 6 grams fat, 5 grams protein, 2 grams carbohydrates)

M1 Caution Modification: Replace half the almond milk with light cream.

M2/Life Modification: Replace all the almond milk with light or heavy cream.

Chocolate Fudge Brownie Sorbet

Naturally dairy free, sorbets are great choices for satisfying desserts. In this version, Capella adds a unique flavor for a super-delicious result.

¾ cup unsweetened cocoa powder
2⅓ cups water

½ tsp. Clear Stevia, or more to taste
6 drops Capella Chocolate Fudge Brownie

1. Place the cocoa powder in a medium bowl and slowly whisk in the water to form a smooth mixture. Whisk in the Stevia and Capella and taste for sweetness.
2. Pour into an ice cream maker, following manufacturer's directions, and process until smooth and thick. *Alternatively, pour the mixture into a 9 x 13-inch metal pan, place in the freezer, and whisk or stir, every 15 minutes, until thick and creamy.*
3. Transfer to an airtight container and keep frozen for up to 1 week.

Makes 8 servings (20 calories; 1 gram fat, 1 gram protein, 5 grams carbohydrates)

M1 Caution Modification: Stir in ¼ cup chopped walnuts or pecans during last 5 minutes.

M2/Life Modification: Stir in ¼ cup crumbled brownie after churning.

Mixed Berry Ice Cream

Summer berries at their peak are perfect for this easy-to-make ice cream that's rich and refreshing.

1½ cups mixed berries
1 tsp. lemon juice
12 drops Sweetleaf Stevia Berry

3 drops Clear Stevia, or more to taste
2 cups unsweetened plain almond milk

1. Place the berries in a medium bowl and use a potato masher to break down the berries into a paste. Stir in the lemon juice and Stevia drops and set aside for 10 minutes.
2. Stir in the almond milk and taste for the addition of Stevia. Pour into an ice cream maker and, following the manufacturer's instructions, churn until thick and creamy. *Alternatively, pour the mixture into a 9 x 13-inch metal pan, place in the freezer, and whisk or stir, every 15 minutes, until thick and creamy.*
3. Transfer to an airtight container and keep frozen for up to 5 days.

Makes 4 servings (44 calories; 1 gram fat, 2 grams protein, 7 grams carbohydrates)

M1 Caution Modification: Replace half the almond milk with light or heavy cream.

M2/Life Modification: Spread the churned mixture into an 8-inch round cake pan and freeze for 2 hours before drizzling with melted chocolate. Serve cut into pie wedges.

Mocha Almond Sherbet

Three great flavors combine for this terrific frozen dessert that's perfect for a sweet after-dinner craving.

2 Tbsp. unsweetened cocoa powder
1 cup water
1 cup unsweetened plain almond milk

8 drops Capella Amaretto
6 drops Capella Cappuccino
½ tsp. Clear Stevia

1. Place the cocoa powder in a medium bowl and slowly whisk in the water until smooth and all lumps are gone. Whisk in the almond milk until well combined, and stir in the Capella and Stevia.
2. Pour into an ice cream maker and, following the manufacturer's instructions, churn until thick and smooth. *Alternatively, pour the mixture into a 9 x 13-inch metal pan, place in the freezer, and whisk or stir, every 15 minutes, until thick and creamy.*
3. Transfer to an airtight container and keep frozen for up to 5 days.

Makes 4 servings (16 calories; 1 gram fat, 1 gram protein, 2 grams carbohydrates)

M1 Caution Modification: Stir 2 Tbsp. sliced almonds into the sherbet during the last 5 minutes.

M2/Life Modification: Replace Amaretto drops with 1 Tbsp. almond liqueur.

Nutty Coconut Frozen Sundaes

The great flavor of sweet coconut highlights these little frozen treats that are great for grabbing on a hot day or when your sweet tooth comes knocking.

¼ cup dried coconut, unsweetened

2 cups unsweetened plain almond milk

½ tsp. Clear Stevia

8 drops Capella Coconut

3 drops Capella Amaretto

1. Place the coconut in a medium nonstick skillet and over medium-high heat, stirring constantly, toast the coconut until golden brown, about 3 minutes. Transfer to a food processor or mini chopper and process until sand-like.
2. In a medium bowl, stir together the almond milk, Stevia, and Capella. Taste for sweetness and stir in all but 2 tsp. of the processed coconut.
3. Pour the milk mixture into an ice cream maker, following manufacturer's directions, and process until smooth and thick. *Alternatively, pour the mixture into a 9 x 13-inch metal pan, place in the freezer, and whisk or stir, every 15 minutes, until thick and creamy.*
4. Transfer to individual paper or plastic cups, sprinkle the reserved coconut on top, and cover each with plastic wrap on the surface. Freeze until firm, about 1 hour, before serving.

Makes 4 servings (45 calories; 3 grams fat, 2 grams protein, 2 grams carbohydrates)

M1 Caution Modification: Replace half the almond milk with unsweetened coconut milk.

M2/Life Modification: Use sweetened shredded coconut in Step 1 and/or stir in 2 Tbsp. toasted sliced almonds during the final minutes of churning.

Baked Desserts

Roasted Peaches and Cream "Crumble"

Quickly roasting fresh peaches adds great flavor and sweetness to this delicious base for an M2/Life traditional crumble version.

4 large peaches
2 tsp. coconut or light olive oil
½ cup water
Juice of ½ an orange
Juice of ½ a lemon
8 drops Capella Peaches & Cream

12 drops Clear Stevia, or more to taste
Dash ground cinnamon
Dash ground nutmeg
Plain unsweetened almond milk for serving, sweetened with Clear Stevia, if desired.

1. Preheat the oven to 400° F.
2. Lightly brush the skins of the whole peaches with the oil and place in a medium roasting pan. Roast in the oven for 45 minutes, occasionally shaking the pan to lightly brown the skins. Remove from the oven and set aside to cool slightly.
3. Using a paring knife, peel away the skin of the peaches and discard. Cut in half, remove the pit, and cut into ½-inch slices. Transfer all the cut peaches to a medium saucepan and add the remaining ingredients except the milk. Bring to a simmer and cook, stirring occasionally, until the peaches are fork tender and the liquid has reduced somewhat. Taste for the addition of Stevia and transfer to a medium gratin dish.
4. Reduce the oven temperature to 375° F and bake until bubbly and browned, about 25 minutes. Cool slightly before serving. Spoon into bowls and serve with a drizzle of almond milk around the edge.

Makes 4 servings (104 calories; 4 grams fat, 2 grams protein, 19 grams carbohydrates)

M1 Caution Modification: Dot with 1 Tbsp. unsalted butter before baking and/or serve with a dollop of whipped heavy cream sweetened with Stevia.

M2/Life Modification: Top with the following crumb mixture: ½ cup whole wheat flour, ¼ cup chopped nuts, 2 Tbsp. unsalted butter, ¼ tsp. Stevia powder or 2 Tbsp. light brown sugar, and bake as directed.

Caramel Baked Pears with Ginger Cream

Sweet delicious pears bake up to perfection with the help of Capella and Stevia in this wonderful and warming autumn dessert that's great any time of year.

1 tsp. coconut oil

4 Bosc pears, peeled, halved, and cored

½ cup unsweetened plain almond milk

6 drops Sweetleaf Stevia Vanilla Crème

3 drops Capella Caramel

1 cup whipped cottage cheese

4 drops Capella Gingerbread

10 drops Clear Stevia, or more to taste

1. Preheat the oven to 375° F. Lightly oil the bottom of a medium glass or ceramic casserole dish.
2. Place the pears cut side down in the dish and bake in the oven for 20 minutes. Meanwhile, combine the almond milk with the Vanilla and Caramel drops and pour over the pears. Continue to bake, occasionally basting, until the pears are fork tender and browned, about 20 minutes more.
3. In a small bowl, beat together the cottage cheese with the remaining ingredients. To serve, place two pear halves on a plate and top with a dollop of the flavored cheese.

Makes 4 servings (145 calories; 5 grams fat, 8 grams protein, 15 grams carbohydrates)

M1 Caution Modification: Replace the cottage cheese with heavy cream and whip with Capella and Stevia.

M2/Life Modification: Drizzle 1 Tbsp. honey over the pears as they roast and top with the sweetened whipped cream, as above.

Lemon Meringue Cookies

Tangy and sweet, these wonderful morsels will definitely delight your taste buds. Try different flavors such as Valencia Orange, Apricot Nectar, or even Chocolate Raspberry!

3 large egg whites
¼ tsp. cream of tartar
⅛ tsp. Clear Stevia

10 drops Sweetleaf Stevia Lemon Drop

1. Preheat the oven to 200° F. Line a baking sheet with parchment paper.
2. In a medium bowl, using an electric mixer, beat the egg whites until frothy. Add the cream of tartar and Stevia and continue to beat until firm peaks form.
3. Spoon 12 mounds of the meringue mixture onto the prepared sheets and bake, rotating the baking sheet from front to back halfway through, for about 40 minutes, until they are firm to the touch.
4. Turn off the oven, open the door a crack, and leave the meringues in the oven to finish drying until crisp.

Makes 4 servings (12 calories; 3 grams protein, 0 grams carbohydrates)

M1 Caution Modification: Make meringue cookie sandwiches by securing 2 cookies together with a dollop of whipped heavy cream flavored with Stevia.

M2/Life Modification: Replace Stevia Lemon Drop with Vanilla Crème and secure 2 cookies together with melted milk, dark, or white chocolate.

Amaretto Macaroons

Moist coconut and delicious Capella Amaretto come together in these marvelous cookies that are perfect for any sweet craving.

1⅓ cups unsweetened shredded coconut

1 Tbsp. Vanilla whey protein powder

½ tsp. salt

8 drops Capella Amaretto

¼ tsp. Clear Stevia, or more to taste

2 large egg whites, slightly beaten

1. Preheat the oven to 325° F. Line a baking sheet with parchment paper.
2. In a medium bowl, toss together the coconut, protein powder, and salt, distributing well. In a small bowl, combine the egg whites, Capella, and Stevia. Stir the egg white mixture into the coconut mixture and drop by full teaspoons onto the prepared pan to form 24 cookies.
3. Bake until the cookies are lightly browned on the edges, about 20 minutes. Transfer the cookies to a wire rack to cool.

Makes 6 servings (72 calories; 9 grams fat, 1 gram protein, 4 grams carbohydrates)

M1 Caution Modification: Substitute almond flour for the protein powder.

M2/Life Modification: Substitute plain flour for the protein powder and use sweetened shredded coconut for half the amount of coconut, adjusting Stevia as needed.

Chocolate Minty Macaroons

Moist and delicious, these treats are delicious and make a great addition to any cookie plate.

1⅓ cups unsweetened shredded coconut

1 Tbsp. Dutch Chocolate whey protein powder

1 Tbsp. unsweetened cocoa powder

½ tsp. salt

6 drops Capella Spearmint

¼ tsp. Clear Stevia, or more to taste

2 large egg whites, slightly beaten

1. Preheat the oven to 325° F. Line a baking sheet with parchment paper.
2. In a medium bowl, toss together the coconut, protein powder, cocoa, and salt, distributing well. In a small bowl, combine the drops with the egg whites. Stir the egg white mixture into the coconut mixture and drop by full teaspoons onto the prepared pan to form 24 cookies (close together is fine).
3. Bake until the cookies are lightly browned on the edges, about 20 minutes. Transfer the cookies to a wire rack to cool.

Makes 6 servings (80 calories; 9 grams fat, 1 gram protein, 4 grams carbohydrates)

M2/Life Modification: Drizzle with melted dark chocolate when cooled.

Scrumptious Strawberry Shortcake

If you think you must wait until M2/Life to enjoy strawberry shortcake, think again. Although strictly a Caution recipe, and not appropriate for early M1 eating, this easy dessert will surprise you with its similarity to the real deal!

For the Shortcake:

> 4 large eggs, separated
> 4 oz. Neufchatel cream cheese
> 8 drops Sweetleaf Stevia Vanilla Crème
>
> Pinch salt
> ¼ tsp. cream of tartar

For the Berries:

> 2 cups fresh strawberries, stemmed and sliced
> 2 Tbsp. water
> 1 tsp. lemon juice
>
> 4 drops Capella Strawberries & Cream
> 10 drops Clear Stevia

1. Preheat the oven to 300° F. Line a baking sheet with parchment paper and set aside.
2. In a medium bowl, using an electric mixer, beat together the egg yolks and Neufchatel until thick and creamy. Beat in the Stevia and set aside.
3. In another medium bowl with clean beaters, beat the egg whites for minute until very frothy. Add the salt and cream of tartar and continue to beat until firm peaks form.
4. Spoon ⅓ of the egg white mixture into the egg yolk mixture and combine well. Spoon the remaining egg white mixture into the bowl and gently fold into the mixture, trying not to lose volume.
5. Using a ½-cup measuring cup, spoon the mixture into 8 piles on the prepared baking sheet an inch apart, distributing the batter equally. Smooth the tops gently with a spatula and bake for 25 to 30 minutes, until set and lightly browned. Remove from the oven and allow to cool on the baking sheet before carefully removing from the parchment.
6. Meanwhile, prepare the berries by combining all the ingredients in a bowl and refrigerate for at least 1 hour, occasionally stirring.
7. To serve, place one shortcake in a bowl, top with ¼ of the berry mixture, and top with another shortcake. Serve immediately.

Makes 4 servings (200 calories; 15 grams fat, 8 grams protein, 8 grams carbohydrates)

(continued on next page)

(continued from previous page)

M1 Caution Modification: Serve with a dollop of whipped heavy cream sweetened with Stevia.

M2/Life Modification: Add sliced banana to the fruit mixture and flavor the shortcakes with Capella Banana.

Chef's Note: Use the shortcake recipe above to make savory buns or rolls by eliminating the Stevia and adding a pinch of ground pepper and/or onion salt. Great for burgers and sandwiches!

Mini Flourless Chocolate Torte

Cooked in the microwave, nothing could be easier than this quick chocolate creation for a fast dessert or snack. With the addition of butter, however, this is definitely a Caution recipe for M1.

1 Tbsp. unsalted butter, melted	$\frac{1}{8}$ tsp. Clear Stevia
2 Tbsp. unsweetened cocoa powder	2 drops Capella French Vanilla
Pinch salt	1 Tbsp. unsweetened plain
1 large egg, slightly beaten	almond milk

1. Lightly oil a 1-cup ramekin or baking dish.
2. In a small bowl, whisk together the butter and cocoa powder until smooth. Whisk in the remaining ingredients to combine well.
3. Pour into the prepared dish and cook in the microwave on high for 1 minute. Set aside to cool and remove from the dish, or serve warm in the ramekin.

Makes 1 serving (210 calories; 18 grams fat, 8 grams protein, 6 grams carbohydrates)

M1 Caution Modification: Replace the almond milk with heavy cream.

M2/Life Modification: Serve warm with a dollop of frozen yogurt or ice cream.

Crustless Marble Cheesecake

This M1 Caution recipe, with the use of cream cheese and heavy cream, is both dreamy and creamy and well worth the wait. Terrific upgrades are possible too!

12 oz. Neufchatel or light cream cheese, softened	3 Tbsp. unsweetened cocoa powder
½ tsp. Clear Stevia, divided	4 drops Sweetleaf Stevia Chocolate
6 drops Capella French Vanilla	1 cup heavy cream, whipped to soft peaks

1. In a medium bowl, beat together the cream cheese, Clear Stevia, and Capella. Transfer half the mixture to another bowl and set aside.
2. Beat the cocoa powder and Stevia Chocolate into the remaining cream cheese mixture. Divide half the whipped cream between both bowls and carefully fold in until combined.
3. Drop dollops of each mixture (vanilla and chocolate) into a glass or ceramic pie plate. Using a knife, cut through the mixture to create a marble effect and smooth out the top. Cover with plastic wrap and refrigerate at least 3 hours before serving.

Makes 8 servings (255 calories; 26 grams fat, 3 grams protein, 3 grams carbohydrates)

M1 Caution Modification: Make a crust by combining ⅔ cup graham cracker crumbs, 1 Tbsp. melted butter, and 8 drops Clear Stevia, and pressing into the pie plate before filling with the cream cheese mixture.

M2/Life Modification: Make a chocolate crumb crust by using ⅔ cup chocolate cookie crumbs in place of the graham cracker crumbs and reduce the Stevia to taste.

HCG Diet Resources

Dr. Simeons' *Pounds & Inches* with a helpful table of contents:
http://www.ThinNow.com/P&I.pdf

Dr. Simeons' *Pound & Inches* in Spanish:
http://www.ThinNow.com/p&i-sp.pdf

The HCG Protocol At-A-Glance:
http://www.ThinNow.com/hcgdietguide.pdf

Chart to track your measurements as your body reshapes:
http://www.ThinNow.com/measurechart.pdf

Highest fat foods to eat on Load Days:
http://www.ThinNow.com/loadfoods.pdf

List of VLCD foods with portions and calories:
http://www.ThinNow.com/vlcdfoods.pdf

List of VLCD foods for vegans and vegetarians:
http://www.ThinNow.com/vegetarian.pdf

List of VLCD-friendly personal care products:
http://www.ThinNow.com/personalcare.pdf

VLCD Food Journals:
http://www.ThinNow.com/food-diary26.pdf
http://www.ThinNow.com/food-diary45.pdf
http://www.ThinNow.com/food-diary60.pdf

Recovering from cheating:
http://www.ThinNow.com/cheatrecovery.pdf

Maintenance 1 (M1) Guide:
http://www.ThinNow.com/m1guide.pdf

Maintenance 2 (M2) Guide:
http://www.ThinNow.com/m2guide.pdf

Journal and tracker for food and calories consumed in M1:
http://www.ThinNow.com/maintenance-journal.pdf

List of starches and what is a starch?
http://www.ThinNow.com/starches.pdf

List of "The Many Faces of Sugar":
http://www.ThinNow.com/sugar.pdf

Conversion chart for substituting Stevia for other sweeteners:
http://www.ThinNow.com/stevia-convert.pdf

Life after the HCG Protocol:
http://www.ThinNow.com/life-after-hcg.pdf

Index by Food Item

Creamy Holiday Eggnog (Maint.),
149
Fizzy Iced Green Tea with Lemon
(VLCD), 5
French Vanilla Cherry Coke
(VLCD), 4
Fruit Punch (VLCD), 4
Green Apple Lemonade (VLCD), 4
Green Tea Spritzer (Maint.), 148
Health Nut Cocktail (Maint.), 145
Herbal Iced Cooler (VLCD), 6
Icy White Tea with Strawberries
(VLCD), 6
Italian Citrus Soda (VLCD), 3
Lemony Lemonade (VLCD), 5
Mock Mountain Dew (VLCD), 4
Orange Ade (VLCD), 5
Orange Delight Iced Tea (VLCD), 5
Peachy Cream Soda (VLCD), 4
Peachy Keen Quaff (Maint.), 147
Peachy Keen Tea (VLCD), 6
Puckered Smooching on the Beach
(VLCD), 5
Rasberry Sparkler (Maint.), 146
Real Ginger Ale (VLCD), 3
Strawberry Ice Cubes (VLCD), 4
Strawberry Kiwi Sangria (Maint.),
148
Super Vanilla Cream Soda (VLCD),
3
Sweet Berry Cherry Cola (VLCD), 4
Tropical Fizz (VLCD), 3
Vanilla Mint Mojito (Maint.), 147
Beverages, hot
Amaretto Cream Latte (VLCD), 10
Apricot and Peach Cobbler Toddy
(VLCD), 11
Blueberry Cinnamon Crumble from
the Oven (VLCD), 12
Caramel Cream Latte (VLCD), 9
Caramel Latte (Maint.), 155
Chamomile Hot Toddy (VLCD), 12
Chocolate Coconut Almond Delight
(Maint.), 157
Chocolate Éclair Latte (VLCD), 9
Chocolate Mint Delight (VLCD), 10

Chocolate Raspberry Café (VLCD),
9
Chocolatey Chai (VLCD), 12
Cinnamon Bun Café (VLCD), 10
Coconut Fudge Latte (VLCD), 9
English Toffee Coffee (VLCD), 9
French Vanilla Café (Maint.), 156
Fresh Rasberry Tisane (Maint.), 153
Gingerbread Chai (Maint.), 154
Gingerbread Latte (VLCD), 10
Green Apple Spiced Cider (VLCD),
11
Hot Spiced Apple Cider (VLCD), 11
Italian Eggnog Latte (VLCD), 10
Lemon Lift Green Tea (VLCD), 10
Melted Peppermint Patty (Maint.),
157
Milk Chocolate Toffee Hazelnut
Latte (VLCD), 9
Minty Irish Cream Coffee (VLCD),
9
Orange Spiced Tea (VLCD), 12
Pralines and Cream Hot Toddy
(VLCD), 11
Pumpkin Chai (Maint.), 154
Pumpkin Spice Latte (VLCD), 10
Spiced Almond Milk (Maint.), 156
Sweet Dark Mocha (VLCD), 9
Sweet Lemon Ginger Tea (VLCD), 11
Tangerine Cinnamon Tea (Maint.),
153
Toasted Marshmallow Cappuccino
(Maint.), 155
Triple Lemon Soother (VLCD), 11
Vanilla Irish Cream Coffee (VLCD),
10
Warm Apple Pie à la Mode (VLCD),
11
Warm Blueberry Cobbler (VLCD),
11
Blackberries
Almond Blackberry Smoothie
(Maint.), 162
Blackberry and Peach Compote
(Maint.), 172

The Ultimate HCG Diet Cookbook

The Ultimate HCG Diet Cookbook

Index by Flavor

Cool Cucumber Tonic (VLCD), 5
Cool Minty Cucumber Soup
(VLCD), 29
Creamy Broccoli Soup (Maint.), 179
Darn Good Deviled Eggs (VLCD), 40
Eggplant Rollatini (Maint.), 243
Eggs à la Benedict (Maint.), 170
Fizzy Iced Green Tea with Lemon
(VLCD), 5
Green Team Spritzer (Maint.), 149
House Italian Dressing (Maint.), 191
Italian Chicken and Escarole Soup
(VLCD), 23
Italian Herbed Stewed Tomatoes
(VLCD), 107
Italian Ice Medley (VLCD), 131
Lemon Egg Drop Soup (VLCD), 25
Lemon Lift Green Tea (VLCD), 10
Lemon Meringue Cookies (Maint.),
260
Lemon-Lime Scrod with Salsa
(Maint.), 227
Lemony Brussels Sprouts (Maint.),
250
Lemony Lemonade (VLCD), 5
Mighty Good Meat-Free Meatloaf
(VLCD), 114
Parma-Style Veal Marinara (Maint.),
219
Petite Baked Crab Cakes (VLCD), 93
Salmon Salad Niçoise (Maint.), 188
Sautéed Lemon Garlic Rainbow
Chard (VLCD), 104
Sensational Salmon Burger (Maint.),
228
Sesame Soy Stir-Fried Asparagus
(VLCD), 102
Spanish-Style Grilled Leeks and
Fennel (Maint.), 245
Spinach Soy Patties with Lemon
Sauce Glaze (VLCD), 117
Stir-Fried Lemon Chicken with
Chard (VLCD), 53
Super Juicy Roast Lemon Chicken
(Maint.), 199
Super Smoked Salmon Scramble
(Maint.), 171

Super Summer Salad with Creamy
Dressing (VLCD), 111
Sweet Lemon Ginger Tea (VLCD), 11
Tangerine Cinnamon Tea (Maint.),
153
Tangy Apple Slaw with Poppy Seeds
(VLCD), 34
Teriyaki Beef with Snow Peas
(Maint.), 214
Teriyaki Sea Bass with Napa
Cabbage (VLCD), 87
Three Alarm Buffalo Tenders
(VLCD), 66
Triple Lemon Soother (VLCD), 11
Tuscan Bistecca with Lemon
(VLCD), 75
Veal Scaloppini with Mock Marsala
Sauce (VLCD), 81

Lemon-Lime, Capella
Cucumber Cilantro Salad (VLCD),
105
Italian Citrus Soda (VLCD), 3
Mock Mountain Dew (VLCD), 4

Marshmallow, Capella
Toasted Marshmallow Cappuccino
(Maint.), 155

Milk Chocolate Toffee, Capella
English Toffee Coffee (VLCD), 9
Milk Chocolate Toffee Hazelnut
Latte (VLCD), 9

Orange Creamsicle, Capella
Asian Chicken Roll Ups (VLCD), 70
Cream of Fennel Soup with Orange
and Coriander (VLCD), 28
Herbal Iced Cooler (VLCD), 6
Italian Citrus Soda (VLCD), 3
Old Time Orange Creamsicle
(VLCD), 129
Orange-Glazed Asparagus (VLCD),
101
Soy Meatballs with Asian Ginger
Orange Sauce (VLCD), 115
Tropical Fizz (VLDC), 3

Spearmint, Capella
Chocolate Minty Macaroons
(Maint.), 262
Cucumber Crunch with Mint and
Cilantro (VLCD), 33
Minty Irish Cream Coffee (VLCD), 9
Strawberry Mint Dressing (VLCD),
46

Strawberries & Cream, Capella
Frozen Strawberries and Cream
(VLCD), 129
Fruit Punch (VLCD), 4
Icy White Tea with Strawberries
(VLCD), 6
Poached Lobster with Strawberry
Vanilla Cream Sauce (VLCD), 96
Scrumptious Strawberry Shortcake
(Maint.), 263
Strawberries and "Cream" Breakfast
Cup (Maint.), 174
Strawberries and Cream Smoothie
(Maint.), 163
Strawberry and Chicken Salad with
Sweet Basil (VLCD), 39
Strawberry Ice Cubes (VLCD), 4
Sweet Strawberry Soufflé Omelet
(VLCD), 110
Very Berry Vinaigrette (VLCD), 45

Sweet Strawberry, Capella
Sautéed Chicken Breast with
Strawberry Compote (VLCD), 55
Strawberry Mint Dressing (VLCD),
46
Super Strawberry Spinach Salad
(VLCD), 35
Sweet Berry Cherry Cola (VLCD), 4
Sweet Strawberry Pancakes (Maint.),
175

Valencia Orange, Sweetleaf Stevia
Asian Chicken Roll Ups (VLCD), 70
Best Sweet and Sour Chicken
(VLCD), 65
Bloody Salsa Maria (Maint.), 145
Chicken with Orange and Fresh
Basil (VLCD), 63

Citrus Thyme Crusted Fish (VLCD),
85
Cream of Fennel Soup with Orange
and Coriander (VLCD), 28
Creamsicle Smoothie (VLCD), 15
Cucumber and Valencia Orange
Salad (VLCD), 33
Easy Onion Frittata (VLCD), 109
Health Nut Cocktail (Maint.), 145
Lemony Brussels Sprouts (Maint.),
250
Napa Sunshine Slaw (Maint.), 184
Orange Ade (VLCD), 5
Orange and Hazelnut Citronette
(VLCD), 46
Orange Banana Smoothie (VLCD), 15
Orange Beef and Asparagus
Negimaki (VLCD), 39
Orange Delight Iced Tea (VLCD), 5
Orange Peach Power Shake (VLCD),
17
Orange Spiced Tea (VLCD), 12
Oven-Roasted Fish with Fennel
(VLCD), 86
Pan-Seared Scallops with Orange
Glaze (Maint.), 236
Quick Chinese Orange Beef (VLCD),
73
Quick Lobster Stir-Fry with Spring
Onions (VLCD), 97
Quick Tartar Sauce (Maint.), 192
Roasted Vegetable Mélange (Maint.),
244
Salmon Salad Niçoise (Maint.), 188
Scalloped Celery and Strawberry
Crisp (VLCD), 103
Seared Ahi Tuna with Wasabi
Dressing (Maint.), 232
Seared Duck Breast with Orange
Sauce (Maint.), 210
Sensational Salmon Burger (Maint.),
228
Silky Shrimp Bisque (Maint.), 181
Soy Meatballs with Asian Ginger
Orange Sauce (VLCD), 115
Spanish-Style Crab Stew (VLCD), 94